MW00338238

Lab Manual
Introduction to
Landforms
2nd edition

By

Paulo J. Hidalgo

Let's

start here.

Kendall Hunt
publishing company

Cover images: Courtesy of the author
Icon graphics within the interior are © Shutterstock, Inc.

Kendall Hunt
p u b l i s h i n g   c o m p a n y

www.kendallhunt.com
Send all inquiries to:
4050 Westmark Drive
Dubuque, IA 52004-1840

Copyright © 2017 by Kendall Hunt Publishing Company
Copyright © 2018 by Paulo Hidalgo-Odio

ISBN 978-1-5249-5070-5

Kendall Hunt Publishing Company has the exclusive rights to
reproduce this work, to prepare derivative works from this work, to
publicly distribute this work, to publicly perform this work and to
publicly display this work.

All rights reserved. No part of this publication may be reproduced,
stored in a retrieval system, or transmitted, in any form or by any
means, electronic, mechanical, photocopying, recording, or
otherwise, without the prior written permission of the copyright
owner.

Published in the United States of America

Table of Contents

THE WAY
WE LEARN

---

words from the author

About this Laboratory Manual

The second edition of this lab handbook is designed to take you out into the world, where landforms exist. The constraints of location and logistics of this course make it difficult and costly to physically take you "out there." For this reason, I have designed a series of activities that will transport you to some of the finest locations to observe a given landform using Google Earth Pro's high-resolution photographs where you will conduct hands on laboratory activities. Google Earth Pro is a tool that simulates Earth by using satellite images. It is coupled with high-resolution photographs taken from lower elevations to create the illusion of being at that location. Furthermore, this software has embedded a tool that allows you to see images from previous years, some dating back to the seventies and even older. This feature allows you to grasp that we live in a dynamic planet that continuously evolves and continuous change is the rule.

This constant change controls everything that we care about, from the origin of life to the climate change that we are experiencing today.

The ultimate goal of this handbook is to make you think about possible applications of this powerful tool. For this reason, you will receive the necessary knowledge to produce your own content. If you dig deep enough, Google Earth Pro cannot only be used to recognize landforms and environmental and sustainability problems, but also to study a wide array of topics from viruses to social issues. I only ask of you to dedicate your time to work on these labs and think about the dynamism of our Planet. We have tremendous power in our hands, but not many understand the interconnectedness of Earth systems. This is shocking, as our long-term survival depends on it.

photo source: Paulo Hidalgo

When teaching becomes a lifetime passion

instructors strive to give students what they need for efficient learning. It is about creating a fertile environment, free of criticism, where students teach themselves, each other, and their instructors. To me teaching is about presenting the current state of the subject, introducing theorems and paradigms (carefully for the faint of heart), and empirical concepts that can be integrated into their own life experiences. Critical thinking and encouraging questions on how this knowledge is integrated into real life situations are crucial to the learning processes.

The troubled times in which we live require responsible citizens and innovative professionals who can navigate through the challenges of our era with resilient determination and unbounded interest who will help solve the problems of our times."

Paulo J. Hidalgo

INTRODUCTION TO GOOGLE EARTH PRO

photo source: NASA

skills

This lab will prepare you for the activities that you will be working on in weeks to come. All the labs in the first few chapters of the book are centered on Google Earth Pro. Therefore, it is vital that you learn how to use this program and its features. Some skills that you will master include navigation, the use of layers, use of featured content, place marks, polygons, and paths. Also, you will find that the ruler tool ▯ will be of great use during these labs. By the end of this activity, you will have obtained proficiency in the use of this fascinating remote sensing tool. Also, you will be able to complete geoscience related projects that require the geographic display of information and hopefully find interesting applications in your daily lives.

Extract and Measure Information

In this lab, you will learn the important skill of extracting and producing data using remote sensing techniques.

Use of Software

Using Google Earth Pro, you will learn how to work with your classmates in interpreting satellite images of our planet.

Communication

This lab will facilitate the practicing of the necessary skills of interpreting, discussing, and sharing data with your learning community.

NOTES

_____

Your Name

Introduction to Google Earth Pro

Pre-Lab Activity

 1- Google Earth Pro is one of many remote sensing techniques. Use your browser to define what remote sensing is. Also, summarize two applications of remote sensing techniques in your major. For more helpful information, open Google Earth Pro. Make sure that in the "Places" panel the "Introduction to Google Earth Pro" lab folder is activated. Expand that folder and activate the "Pre-lab" folder. Click on "Link 1" under "Pre-lab" for guidance.

Remote sensing:

_____

_____

_____

_____

Application 1:

_____

_____

_____

Application 2:

_____

_____

 2-First, you will be using your internet browser. Open the Google Earth User's Guide by clicking on "Link 2" found in the "Pre-lab" folder.

Using the figure on the next page and aided by the user guide, locate with arrows the following items: 1. Menu, 2. Toolbar, 3. Navigation controls, 4. Places panel, 5. Layers panel, 6. Latitude–longitude–elevation, and 7. Viewing elevation. *Keep in mind the Google Earth status bar showing latitude, longitude, etc., is viewed at the bottom when the Tour Guide is closed.

_____

_____

_____

_____

_____

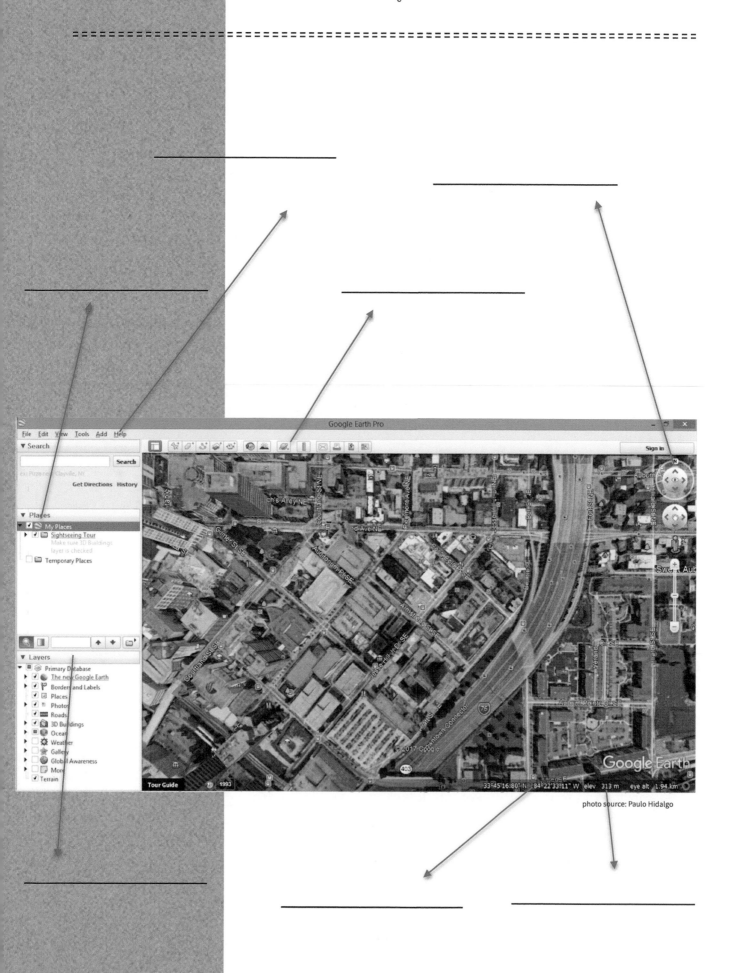

photo source: Paulo Hidalgo

_____

_____

_____

===

 3- Using the figure below, indicate with arrows the location in the toolbar of: 1. Hide/Show side bar, 2. Add polygon, 3. Add placemark, 4. Add path, 5. Show historical imagery, 6. Switch between Earth, sky, and planets, 7. Ruler tool, and 8. E-mail.

 4- The navigation panel will let you control the position of your view of the Earth. Indicate the functions of each of the tools in this panel; use the arrows to guide you.

_____

_____

_____

_____

NOTES

In-Lab Activity 1

In this part, you will learn how to take snapshots of items of interest in Google Earth Pro. The goal is to produce a screenshot of the Appalachian Mountain range in a three-dimensional (3D) view as seen from the South.

Step 1- Navigation

The initial step is to figure out how the navigational controls operate. Let us start by zooming in and out and panning around using all the different controls.

Step 2- Point of interest

Now "fly to" "Mount Mitchell," the highest point of the Appalachians by typing "Mount Mitchell" in the search panel. The method to get a good snapshot of an elevated point of interest is to get a good vantage for seeing in 3D. It helps to be around the level of the highest topography. Zoom in using the "+" until you are at about the "eye alt" of Mt Mitchell. You can find the "eye alt" in the lower right corner of the Google Earth Pro window.

Step 3- Rotate

Next, rotate your view so that you are looking towards the North instead of straight down. You can achieve this by clicking the "^" closest to the North "N" indicator.

Step 4- Pan

Now, move to the South away from Mount Mitchell to get a better viewpoint. You should see that you are moving away from the highest mountains.

Step 5- Vertical Scale

You can make a sensational image by increasing the vertical exaggeration in Google Earth Pro. Go to Tools—>Options—>Terrain panel and set "Elevation Exaggeration" to "3" from "1." You may need to zoom out to reorient your image after this step.

Step 6- Snap Picture

Finally, take a screenshot in Google Earth Pro by pressing and holding down the "ctrl" and "prt sc" keys on your computer's keyboard. Then, open up the Paint application on your computer, press paste, and feel free to crop undesired borders in your screenshot using Paint or a similar application.

In-Lab Activity 2

In this exercise you will learn how to make topographic profiles . To understand what a topographic profile is, click "Link 1" under the "In-lab Activity 2" places folder.

1- In your own words describe what is a topographic profile (also known as a cross section).

_____

_____

_____

_____

Now that you know what a topographic profile is, create your own by following these steps:

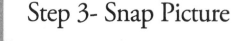 **Show an Elevation Profile across the State of Georgia**

Step 1- Create a Path

To make a cross section through the state, start by adding a path. You can do this by using the path tool "Add path"(check User Guide if you are not sure how). With this tool draw a line from north (Tennessee–Georgia border) to south (Georgia's coast) passing through Atlanta. Give it a name before you click OK.

Step 2- Create Elevation Profile

In "Places" (side panel), right-click on the name of the line section you just made and select "Show Elevation Profile."

Step 3- Snap Picture

Make a screen capture of the profile and save it to the desktop. Note: utilize the Paint application's cropping tool to crop your elevation profile from the overall screenshot you took. E-mail the two images that you created to your teaching assistant (TA) including the names of any partners that you had during this assignment.

==

🧪 In-Lab Activity 3

In Google Earth Pro, the content is organized on the left side of the screen (Search, Places, Layers). By clicking on the Layers panel, you can turn on and off features such as roads, name of places, city, state, county boundaries, and other content. You will find that as you zoom in the Google Earth screen, more of these icons will pop up. This is what is called "featured content." This content has been created by Google and other users like you.

> *Notice within the Layers panel there is a "Gallery" folder. Click the arrow next to "Gallery" to expand the folder. Now we are going to activate some of the content within "Gallery." Once expanded, activate (click) the box next to "Gigapxl Photos." Gigapixel photos are high-resolution photos taken in certain locations on Earth. Make sure all other content boxes within "Gallery" are deselected to avoid confusion when examining just the gigapixel photos.*

1- In the search panel, type "Mount Saint Helens National Monument" and press "enter." You will be transported to this national monument, which is located in the state of _____.
Find the gigapixel photo north of this monument and double-click on its icon. You will see that a description of this monument will pop up. Read it and then click "fly into this ultra high-resolution photo." You will find that you can zoom in and out of the photograph. Play with the zoom and test how far you can zoom in. One of the more striking features in the photograph is a large crater on the side of Mount St. Helens. In some books, this is described as a sector collapse. Based on the description of this image that you read previously, how and when did this crater form? In your answer indicate in what direction this crater is facing.

_____
_____
_____
_____
_____

2- You can see what appears to be a series of linear features in the foreground on the side of the green hill. This area can be described to have a "matchstick-like" pattern. Zoom in as much as possible to determine what the multiple long objects are. Theorize about how this array was formed. Write your answer below.

_____
_____
_____
_____

In-Lab Activity 4

Exit the photo and turn the gigapixel layer off (uncheck the box). Zoom out until you can see the highest point of the volcano. Click the "N" on the control panel ring. This will reorient the map.You are now ready to create your content for sharing.

 Before you start recording your work, click once on "my places" in the "places" panel in the sidebar. Using the "Add" menu at the top of the Google Earth menu click on the folder. Name this folder with your last names in alphabetical order. For example, if Ms. Jed I. Knight and Mr.Chris P. Bacon were working together on this project, the folder would be called "KnightBacon." Now you should see your folder in the "places" area, if not move the folder if needed, simply drag and drop to reposition the folders.

Create your own content

Step 1- Create a Placemark

Click the icon for "placemark". This action will add a placemark to your folder. You can name the placemark as you please. DO NOT yet close the Placemark window! Now is the moment to reposition the placemark to the center of the crater. You can add a description to your placemark. Add a description that is no more than 100 words long using the observations that you have collected so far. Before you are done with your placemark, you have the option of changing the symbol for your placemark. You can achieve this by clicking on the current symbol of the placemark in the pop-up window and choosing the volcano symbol for your placemark. Click OK.

You will see that your new placemark has appeared in the folder you created (If not, drag and drop). If you want to edit your placemark, you may right-click on the placemark you just created and select "properties."

Step 2- GSU Placemark

Find Georgia State University, either by searching or by using the control panel to "fly" to it. You may be able to navigate better if you activate in the "Layers" panel the "Road" box. While you are at it, make sure the "3D Buildings" box is activated. Add a placemark in the center of Kell Hall. Give the placemark a name, description, and an interesting icon. Make sure the placemark is located inside your folder in the "Places" panel. If not, move it by dragging and dropping.

Step 3- Create a Path

Now, add a path displaying the most likely route by foot from your icon on Kell Hall to the NE corner of Hurt Park (Courtland St. and Edgewood Ave. corner). Click on the icon to add a path (see the left panel). Do not forget to give the path a name and a description. To create the path, click your starting point and then click along the chosen route to your destination. When you are done with the clicking, select a vivid color for your route, so it displays distinctively.

Step 4- Create a Polygon, calculate area

Select a dorm on campus. In this part of the lab, you will use the "polygon" tool to show where this building is located. Click the icon in the tools menu. Do not forget to give the polygon a name and a short description. Clicking at each corner of the building allows you to create a polygon. Be sure to close the polygon by connecting the first point to the last point. Now, in the "Properties" window for the polygon, give the polygon color and change the line color. Adjust the area opacity to 50%. Under the "Altitude" Tab, "select relative to the ground" on the drop down menu and give the polygon an altitude of "30 m." Click "ok." By using the navigation control panel, tilt the view to show the 3D view of the polygon. Right-click on the name of your polygon, then click on "Snapshot View." This means that whenever someone clicks on your polygon, they will be shown the same view that you have just designated.

Click on the properties of this polygon and measure the dorm area. What is it?
_____m²

Step 5- Calculate distance

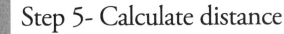

In the tools panel, select the ruler tool and measure the distance in **meters** from the center of Library South to the center of the fountain in Hurt Park in a straight line. What is it?
_____m

Step 6- Compare and Contrast

Is this satellite image of Georgia State University current (showing what the campus looks like now)? How do you know? Give at least two lines of reasoning.

_____
_____
_____
_____

Click on the "show historical imagery icon" and indicate two changes in the city of Atlanta since 1993 (example: look at the Turner Field area).

_____
_____
_____
_____
_____

NOTES

NOTES

LATITUDE, LONGITUDE, AND MAPS

2

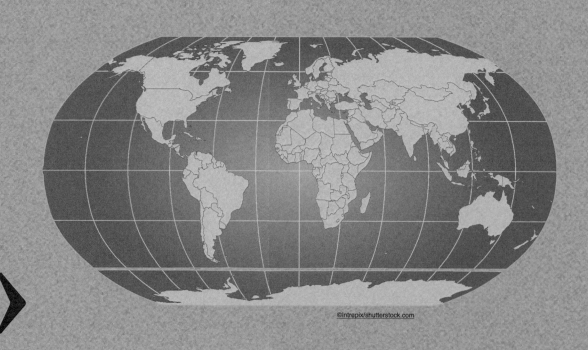

»

©Intrepix/shutterstock.com

Skills

Imagine that your best friend calls you asking for your help because his/her car broke down. You get the location and barely have enough battery on your phone to finish your conversation. Luckily, you have a road map of Georgia in your backseat to guide you to the location. To safely navigate to the place you will need to know about landmarks, distances, direction to the geographic north, and topography. Geoscientists commonly face such conditions when they are out and about recording, cataloging, and sampling natural phenomena. They need to carefully register features and the places where they occur. Often, they have to describe the sizes of those features, shapes, elevations, and locations about other points of interest. They rely on maps, satellite images, and aerial photographs to aid them. During today's lab, you will get a first-hand experience of the work that an Earth scientist does to investigate the natural realm.

_____ ## Use of Maps
Build your spatial reasoning and make sense of our world by working in this lab.

_____ ## Understand Time zones
In this lab you will understand why we have different time zones around the world and other interesting concepts.

_____ ## Map Scales
Working on this lab, you will be exposed to the concept of map scales and how to use them for our benefit.

_____ ## Communicating
This lab will facilitate the practicing of the important skills of interpreting, discussing, and sharing data with your learning community.

NOTES

Pre-Lab Activity

The first part of this lab is designed to help you get familiar with maps and how we use them to find locations and other useful information. In this section, a series of terms will be presented to you. You may need to consult the internet or your textbook to define the terms. Alternatively, you may watch a video by making sure the "Latitude and Longitude" lab is activated in Google Earth Pro. Expand the "Latitude and Longitude" folder, click to expand the "Pre-lab folder," and click "Link 1."

1- Define the following terms and provide sketches illustrating your definitions. Use the boxes for your drawings.

Equator

_____

_____

_____

Prime Meridian

_____

_____

_____

Hemisphere

_____

_____

_____

A Line of Latitude

_____

_____

_____

_____

A Line of Longitude

_____

_____

_____

To represent geographical features on a map (such as a building), the features must be reduced in size (of course!). This is called scaling. How much these features are reduced is known as the map's scale. It gives a relationship between map distance (measured in the map) and ground distance. All maps have a scale.

 2- In the lower right figure, the length of the phone is 10 cm. The real phone has a length of 20 cm. This means that the phone dimensions are two times larger in real life than in this drawing, or that the drawing is 1/2 the size of the real phone.

$$\frac{\text{Length of the real phone}}{\text{Length of the phone in the diagram}} = \frac{20 \text{ cm}}{10 \text{ cm}}$$

In the figure below, the distance between the Court House and the school in the map is 6 cm. In the ground that distance is 6 km (or 600,000 cm, given that there is 100 cm in every meter and 1,000 m in every kilometer).

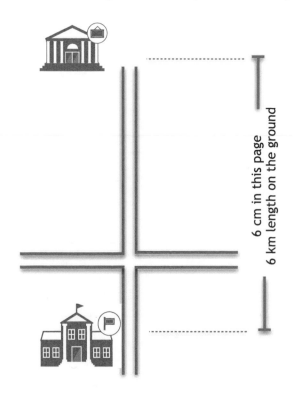

6 cm in this page
6 km length on the ground

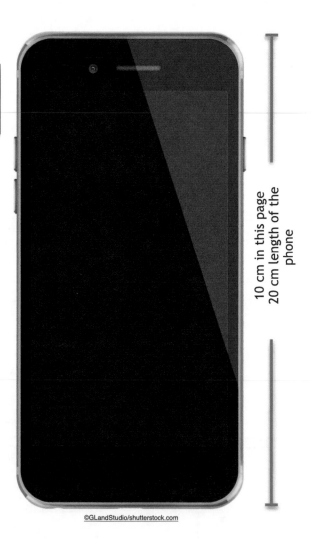

10 cm in this page
20 cm length of the phone

©GLandStudio/shutterstock.com

===

$$\frac{\text{Length on the ground}}{\text{Length on the map}} = \frac{600{,}000 \text{ cm}}{6 \text{ cm}} = 100{,}000$$

Scale of the Map is 1:100,000

Hence, the scale is 1/100,000 (no units). This means that 1 cm on the map is equal to 100,000 cm on the ground.

If we have a different map of the same area that has a scale of 1/50,000, will the courthouse be larger or smaller in that map? Explain your reasoning.

_____

_____

_____

_____

_____

3- Explain what does it mean when people talk about high and low latitude. What are the maximum values of latitude on Earth and where are they located? How about longitude?

_____

_____

_____

_____

_____

4- Click on "Question 4" in Google Earth Pro. Use this location to calculate the scale of the map that you see in your screen. DO NOT ZOOM IN/OUT. You need a ruler to answer this question. Show your work here.

NOTES

In-Lab Activity 1

This section will get you acquainted with latitude and longitude determinations. For this purpose, expand the "Latitude and Longitude" folder. You will see another folder called "In-Lab Activity 1," expand that folder in addition to the one labeled "Question 1." Make sure you zoom in to get more accurate readings.

1. Use the Google Earth place marks in the "Question 1" folder to complete the following table.

Description of locations	Latitude	Longitude	Elevation (m)
LOCATION A			
LOCATION B			
LOCATION C			
LOCATION D			

Use the Google Earth search bar and draw what you see at the following locations. As you can see many formats for coordinates can be used. This will be very handy in upcoming labs.

26.357896, 127.783809	27°22'50.10"N, 33°37'54.62"E	33.747252, -112.633853	-33.867886, -63.987

41.303921, -81.901693	19°56'56.96"S 69°38'1.83"W (ZOOM IN!!!!)

==

> 💡 *The next question will get you familiarized with how latitude and longitude vary across the globe. In the "In-Lab Activity 1" folder open the folder labeled "Question 2."*

2-As you move south of the equator how does the latitude change? As you move north of the equator how does the latitude change? As you travel west of the Prime Meridian how does longitude change? As you travel to the east of the Prime Meridian how does the longitude change? Note: activate latitude/longitude lines pressing "Ctrl"+"L" once at the same time.

_____

_____

_____

_____

_____

_____

3- Open and activate the "Question 3" folder.
a. Double-click on the location included in this folder and indicate which two lines intersect at that location.

_____

b.   Measure the equatorial circumference of Earth. Select the ruler tool and measure 1 degree to the East on the Equator. For example, measure the distance from 0 E to 1 E (to check if your measurement is 1 degree, in the ruler box you can select to measure by degrees!).

Take this value in km and multiply it by 360 (since there are 360 degrees in a circle). What is the equatorial circumference of Earth in km? What is the polar circumference of Earth in km? Here is some space to explain your calculations:

Equatorial Circumference: _____Polar Circumference_____

⏱ In-Lab Activity 2

This section will help you answer why we have differences in the time of day depending on where we are. You will realize that some locations could have more than 24 hours of difference compared to your present location! You will learn to calculate the time in any location in the world! Also, you will realize the importance of having time zones and why it is important that we know how to calculate time differences between countries.

> 💡 *You need to be aware of some general facts before proceeding with this section: 1. It takes 24 hr for the Earth to rotate once; 2. Time zones are an international agreement; 3. Time zones are based on political boundaries; 4. The international date line is an imaginary line beyond which the date changes; 5. The international dateline is located at about 180 degrees of longitude but deviates to pass around some territories; and 6. The Earth has been divided into 24 time zones.*

1.   You know that there are 24 h in each day (hence, 24 time zones). How many degrees separate two consecutive time zones? Explain your reasoning.

_____

_____

_____

2. In Google Earth activate "In-Lab Activity 2." Day – 12:00 a.m. or midnight – begins at 0 longitude – which is called_____. All global time is based on that time zone. You can see that Greenwich, England is in the 0-degree time zone. Zero degrees longitude would run down the center of this zone. Indicate how many hours and degrees away is International Date Line? Explain your reasoning.

_____

_____

_____

> 🗨 *Activate the "International Time zone" overlay in the "In-Lab Activity 2" folder. You may zoom in and out of this image. In this image, time zones are identified by how many hours before (to the left) or after (to the right) as compared to Greenwich time. So, for example, if it is 2:00 p.m. in England, Italy is "+1" or 1 hr later: 3:00 p.m., and the West coast of the United States is "–8" or 8 h earlier: 6:00 a.m.*

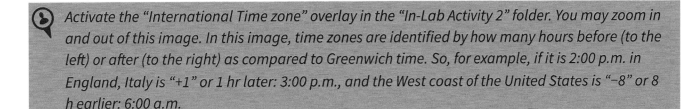

3.   Make sure the "International Time zone" overlay in Google Earth is activated and answer the following questions. Use your Google Earth to help identify countries if needed. Remember that you must indicate a.m. or p.m. As you know a.m. means_____ and p.m. means_____.

a.   If it is noon in Greenwich, England what time is it in Atlanta?
_____

b.   If it is 2:00 p.m. in Greenwich, England what time is it in Iraq?
_____

c.   If it is 3:00 p.m. in New Orleans, LA what time is it in Kathmandu?
_____

d.   How many time zones are in the United States and what is the name of your time zone?_____

🌍 In-Lab Activity 3

After completing this section, you will be able to understand the differences between maps and other surface representations as well as understand the concept of scale and correlate distances in maps with distances on the ground. In Google Earth, the scale of the map that is displayed in the main window changes as you zoom in and out. In the broad sense, we call a "large-scale map" a map where there is a small surface area being represented and the detail of that area in the map is large. In contrast, a "small-scale map" represents a large area that does not have a lot of detail. Let us practice some of these concepts.

Before starting this section, make sure that the graphical scale in Google Earth is visible in the lower left corner. If not, click on the "view" menu and activate "Scale legend." This legend will only be visible if you have the adequate zoom (i.e., is not visible if your eye altitude is far from the ground).

1- In the search panel, type Atlanta, Georgia and press return. Describe four natural or human-made features that you can observe at this scale.

_____
_____
_____
_____
_____

==

🔍 2- In the search panel, type the name of your hometown. You may need to type the state's name too. Describe four features that you can see.

_____
_____
_____
_____

🔍 3- Which map shows more area (question 1 or 2)? Which one shows more detail? At what scale is your hometown visible? And at what scale is your elementary school visible?

_____
_____
_____
_____
_____
_____

📡 In-Lab Activity 4

On the next page, you can see a series of images that are used in the field of remote sensing. Remote sensing is the science of obtaining information about objects or areas from a distance. This is typically done using satellites or aircraft.

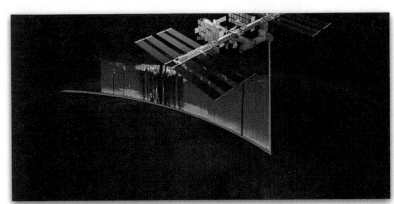

photo source: NASA

Satellites are important tools used by NASA for remote sensing. The first types of remote sensing involved people taking pictures from hot air balloons.

 The first image on the next page shows a topographic map (A) that uses contour lines to show landforms. It is widely used to make accurate measurements of elevation, distances, and directions in the field. B. Aerial photographs are taken from a plane. C. Landsat images are made by satellites taking images of the Earth using different wavelengths of the electromagnetic spectra (e.g. infrared is preferred for observing vegetation). D. Digital elevation maps are computer generated 3D views of landforms made with radar. As you can imagine each of these has different applications.

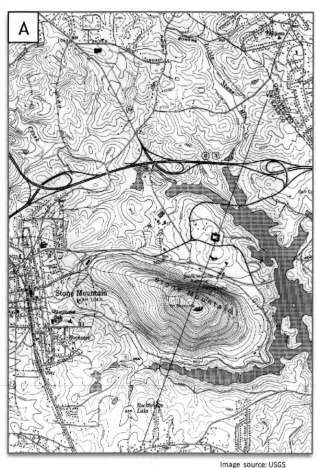

Image source: USGS

photo source: USGS

photo source: NASA

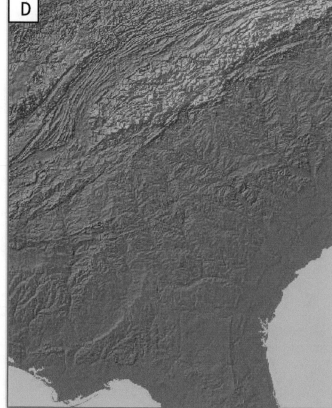

Image source: NASA

==

1. Explain which one will be most helpful to identify hills, valleys, and bodies of water.

_____

_____

_____

_____

_____

2. If you are interested in the distribution of highways and roads, which one will you use and why? Will your answer be different if you were interested in unpaved roads?

_____

_____

_____

_____

_____

3. The technologies to produce these images appeared at different times in human history. Order these pictures according to their appearance in land surveys. Explain your reasoning.

_____

_____

_____

_____

_____

4. You are planning a wilderness hike this weekend in this area. Which image would you want to have? Why?

_____

_____

_____

_____

_____

5. Which image represents a larger area? Which image represents the smallest area? Which image has the largest scale, which one has the smallest scale? Explain the relationship between area and scale size.

_____

_____

_____

_____

_____

NOTES

NOTES

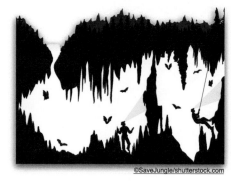

©SaveJungle/shutterstock.com

3

WEATHERING AND KARST LANDFORMS

Objectives

The purpose of this lab is to familiarize you with the processes of physical and chemical weathering, as well as karst landscapes. Secondary objectives include exploring the dynamic nature of these processes and how weathering/karst landscapes change over geologic time due to different global conditions such as atmospheric composition, urbanization, etc.

Concepts

⌄	⌄	⌄	⌄
Physical Weathering	Chemical Weathering	Karst Topography	Caves and Speleothems

Core Concepts

photo source: Paulo Hidalgo

photo source: Paulo Hidalgo

photo source: Paulo Hidalgo

Physical Weathering
Temperature and potential energy

Chemical Weathering
Water abundance, high temperature

Karsts
High dissolution rates, high PH

Frost Wedging
⟶

Salt Wedging
⟶

Thermal Expansion
⟶

Exfoliation
⟶

Abrasion
⟶

Dissolution
⟶

Hydrolisis
⟶

Hydration
⟶

Oxidation
⟶

Karst Topography
⟶

Role of Dissolution
⟶

Caves
⟶

Disappearing Streams
⟶

Learning outcomes

After completing this lab, you should be able to hypothesize what types of weathering may be present in an area. You will realize the important role that weathering plays in both forming sedimentary rocks and ocean salinity. Also, you will realize that there are recognizable superficial signs of underground karst topography. Ultimately, you will learn the basic chemistry at work during the weathering of Earth's materials.

NOTES

Weathering types

> 💡 *This section will get you acquainted with the types of weathering. For this purpose, open Google Earth Pro. Make sure that in the "Places" panel the "Weathering Lab" is activated. Expand the "Weathering Lab" folder. You will see another folder called "Pre-lab," expand the folder. Click on the "Learning Module 1" and "Learning Module 2" links under "Placemark 1.1." Use your book as well the info from the animations to answer the following questions.*

Pre-Lab Activity

1- After you have observed the animations and have studied their content, describe which type of physical weathering would most likely occur along a coastline? Explain your answer.

_____

_____

_____

_____

_____

2- Carbon dioxide (CO_2) levels were much higher in the Jurassic than they are today. Which type of chemical weathering would have been more prevalent as a result of the Jurassic's heightened CO_2 levels? (Hint: In the animation, check the text associated with chemical weathering that is related to dissolution). Explain your answer.

_____

_____

_____

_____

3- Name an environment where thermal expansion would occur most dramatically. Explain your answer.

_____

_____

_____

_____

_____

4- Based on the animation, which area is experiencing the greatest amount of weathering and why? Include in your answer a description of the thickness of the soil profile (activate photo "soils and climate" if you need help). Would the soil horizons be thick or thin?

_____

_____

_____

_____

_____

5- Based on the photo "soils and climate," which area is experiencing the least amount of weathering? Explain your answer.

_____

_____

_____

_____

_____

_____

6-The Piedmont region in Georgia (where Atlanta sits) is characterized by metamorphic rocks that have a great abundance of iron. Which type of chemical weathering would you expect to be the most common and why?

_____

_____

_____

_____

_____

This rock outcrop close to Atlanta, Georgia, has abundant iron. Weathering processes have turn the coloration of this rock to tones of red.

photo source: Paulo Hidalgo

7-Which type of chemical weathering occurs when H_2O chemically reacts with minerals to produce different compounds? Explain your answer.

_____

_____

_____

_____

_____

==

8- Limestone is a sedimentary rock composed of the mineral calcite ($CaCO_3$). What type of landform occurs when underground limestone is dissolved by acidic groundwater? And why?

_____

_____

_____

_____

_____

An example of this weathering landscape is found by clicking Placemark 1.1. Where is this Landscape?_____

9- *Double-click on "Placemark 1.2".* The photo from was taken at_____.
In this salt-rich environment, there are abundant sandstone outcrops that are broken down into the honeycomb-like structures seen in the photo. What type of weathering produces these types of structures?

_____

_____

_____

_____

_____

NOTES

_____

 # In-Lab Activity 1

This section will give you the basic definitions that you will need throughout the lab.

 Weathering not only breaks rocks down, it also provides the necessary material for the production of new rocks. The following terms are very handy when describing weathering

precipitate	**transported**	**physical weathering**	**lithification**
compacted	**deposition**	**sedimentary rock**	**chemical weathering**

1- Fill in the blanks using the words from the word bank above. Use each term only once.

_____ is the mechanical breakdown of rock into smaller chunks of sediment, or clasts. _____ is the decomposition of Earth materials by which dissolved ions and secondary minerals, such as clays, are leached from parent rock. The_____ of weathering are sediment, secondary minerals, and dissolved ions. The sediment and secondary minerals released by weathering erode away and are_____ by water and air until they settle out, a process called_____. Over time, these sediments and secondary minerals become buried and are _____ by the weight of the overlying material. The ions released by chemical weathering (commonly SiO_2 and $CaCO_3$) are transported and _____ out of water to become cement. This cement acts like glue to hold the sediment together as consolidated_____. Transformation of loose sediment into solid rock is a process known as _____.

The following samples were taken from the Flint River (in Georgia) before and after a storm. After analyses, the composition for both samples was found to be the same once the solid clay-size particles suspended in the second sample were separated. The composition was predominantly minor amounts of: Ca, Mg, HCO_3^-, and sulfates dissolved in water.

©Alena Brozova/shutterstock.com

===

Q 1- .Hilly topography is characteristic this landform type. It may be helpful at this location to fly around and find multiple viewing angles to get a better feel for the topography. You may click "Karst" under word bank for another example.

Coordinates of this site: _____

Landform: _____

Weathering Type: _____

       a- Use photos 1 to 3 (In "Location 1") to answer the following:
Do disappearing streams really 'disappear?' Explain what is meant by the term disappearing stream. Where do these streams 'reappear?'

_____

_____

_____

_____

_____

_____

       b. Click on the "Stalactites" photo to answer the following question. Speleothems are a type of cave structures that precipitate from the roofs and floors of caves. Stalactites hang from cave ceilings, stalagmites jut from the ground, and columns are formed when a stalactite and a stalagmite connect. Draw a cave with stalactites, stalagmites, and a column in the space below and label them.

Click on "Sinkhole Animation" under "In-Lab Activity 2" for a bit of info on sinkholes. (You may need to click "watch on chrome" to see the animation properly.) After the video, Double-click on "Arecibo Observatory".

==

Q 2- The Arecibo Observatory is a reclaimed karst sinkhole. This radio telescope is the largest curved focusing dish on Earth. Measure its depth in meters using the elevation indicator in the lower right-hand corner of the Google Earth window. Measure depth along the orange line by recording elevation changes from top to bottom. Alternatively, you can right-click on this line in the "Places" panel and select "Show elevation profile."

_____

_____

Double-click on "Monument Valley, AZ" . Click on "Up Close" to see a detailed photo.

Q 3- .Monument Valley is a part of the Colorado Plateau on the border of Utah and Arizona. The red floor of the valley is largely due to exposed iron oxide in weathered siltstone. Monument Valley also contains a Navajo Tribal Park of the Navajo Nation. Fill in the blanks using the word bank suggested above.

Coordinates of this site: _____

Landform: _____

Weathering Type: _____

a- Explain the weathering process at work on this landform.

_____
_____
_____

b. Why are these landforms more gradually sloping near their base?

_____
_____

Double-click on "Malham Karst, UK" Click on "Up Close" to see a detailed photo. Click back to Google Earth to answer question 4.

Q 4- Malham North Yorkshire, England is right in the middle of the UK. Malham is famous for its incredibly scenic outcrops of limestone pavement. Use the ruler at the top of the Google Earth window to measure the area of limestone pavement indicated by the red polygon. Measure the area in square meters.

_____

_____

===

Double-click on "Stone Mountain, GA". Click on "Up Close" to see a detailed photo. For another example click on "Enchanted Rock, TX Photo."

5- .Stone Mountain is a batholith or an igneous (volcanic) rock body that formed under the Earth's surface. Millions of years of uplift and erosion uncovered Stone Mountain and exposed it to weathering (this is visible on its surface today). Fill in the blanks using the word bank suggested above.

Coordinates of this site: _____

Landform: _____

Weathering Type: _____

The granite that makes up Stone Mountain is a rock that is made up of quartz, mica, and feldspar. Quartz is very resistant to chemical weathering; the other minerals, however, are more vulnerable to chemical weathering. The chemical weathering of the vulnerable minerals produces clays and ions. The clays are eroded away and are transported through rivers until they settle out, a process called deposition. The ions, Na and K, are eroded away and are transported to the ocean.

a. What becomes of the ions that make it to the ocean? Click on "ocean water" for help answering this question.

_____

_____

Double-click on "Dunkeld Peak". Click on "Up Close" to see a detailed photo.

6- Dunkeld Peak is a part of the Coast Mountains in British Columbia. Located in the southwest of the region, just northwest of Washington State. In the colder months, temperatures in this area regularly cycle above and below freezing. Fill in the blanks using the word bank suggested above.

Coordinates of this site: _____

Landform: _____

Weathering Type: _____

a. Would the weathering process affecting this type of landform be more effective in an area with freezing temperatures year round or in an area with temperatures that cycle above and below freezing? Why?

_____

_____

_____

_____

In-Lab Activity 3

Without an atmosphere, many of the processes that both physically and chemically weather rocks will not occur. Earth has an atmosphere, which contains hydrogen and nitrogen primarily. Earth's atmosphere also contains water vapor and CO_2. These gases are responsible for much of the chemical weathering such as dissolution, which relies on the presence of H_2O and CO_2. Oxidation occurs when iron-rich rocks are exposed to oxygen and water. Without the water cycle, a feature of our active atmosphere, no frost wedging or crystal wedging can occur. Practically zero chemical weathering takes place without the presence of liquid water. What is weathering like on planetary bodies that have drastically different atmospheric environments?

Q 1- Mercury: An atmosphere not only regulates temperature and produces weather, but it also serves as friction to help burn up and break down comets and meteors. Mercury's atmosphere, being as thin and scarce as it is, does very little to burn up space debris entering its orbit. This bombardment of space debris, called space weathering, coupled with the relative absence of other types of weathering would result in what kind of landscape on Mercury? Explain the relative permanence of this landscape (think about what erases weathering indicators on Earth).

_____

_____

_____

_____

_____

Q 2- Mercury has nearly no atmosphere. However, the temperatures can range from 800°F to 330°F. Such extreme temperature shifts would result in what type of mechanical weathering? Compare the weathering processes on Mercury with those of the Earth.

_____

_____

_____

_____

_____

_____

_____

==

The moon lacks an abundant atmosphere, and thus temperatures vary widely in comparison to Earth. Temperatures on the moon can reach as low as −387°F on the dark side, and as high as 253°F in the sun. The moon lacks a water cycle; therefore chemical weathering is nearly nonexistent. The process most commonly at work on rocks on the moon is meteor impact or space weathering. This space weathering has led to a lunar surface that is nearly a kilometer deep in loose, broken rock fragments called regolith.

 Click on the little planet icon near the top of the Google Earth window. It will bring up a pull down menu. Select the Moon. Double-click on "The Moon" under In-Lab Activity 3" to be flown to a lunar surface pockmarked by impact craters.

3- You will need to use the ruler tool. Use the ruler to measure, in kilometers, the diameter of this crater. Write the name of the crater and the measurements here:

_____

*The Chicxulub crater responsible for the extinction of the dinosaurs has a diameter of 180

4- Compare the weathering processes at work on both the moon and Mercury.

_____
_____
_____
_____
_____
_____
_____

Mars: The Martian atmosphere is thicker than that of Mercury and the Moon but is much thinner than that of the Earth. There is almost no liquid water on Mars, and as a result, chemical weathering is practically nonexistent. However, Mars is covered in rust, which forms during oxidation (a type of chemical weathering) when the iron is exposed to water and air. There is evidence that ancient Mars may have contained a substantial amount of liquid water. Click "Mars fly-by" if you want to see a video of the Martian surface.

5- Why is no new rust forming on Mars? What does this say about the rust that is present today on Mars?

_____
_____
_____
_____
_____

NOTES

PLATE TECTONICS 4

How the Earth Works

©robin2/shutterstock.com

Continental Drift

The belief that continents have not always been fixed in their present positions is the core of the theory of continental drift. This is an essential component of the plate tectonic theory. It was first proposed in 1915 and was not accepted until the 1960's.

Plate Tectonic Theory

A plate is a large, rigid slab of solid rock. The word tectonics comes from the Greek root "to build." Putting these two words together, we get the term plate tectonics, which refers to how the Earth's surface is built of plates.

Skills

The plate tectonic theory is a robust, testable model that interprets and predicts the surface motions of the Earth's lithosphere. Scientists developed this geological model through rigorous evaluations of many lines of evidence. The exercises presented here aim to help you experience the process of conducting science and to understand the science underlying the plate tectonic theory. In this lab, you will learn to synthesize several datasets to determine the characteristics and locations of plate boundaries. Also, you will be able to predict the type of tectonic plate boundary using bathymetry, earthquake, volcano, and seafloor age data. At the end, you will be able to predict plate motion rates and directions by examining an unfamiliar plate setting.

Evidence for Plate Tectonics

Fit of the continents

Location of past glaciations

Distribution of climatic belts

Distribution of fossils

Matching geologic units and mountain belts

Seafloor spreading

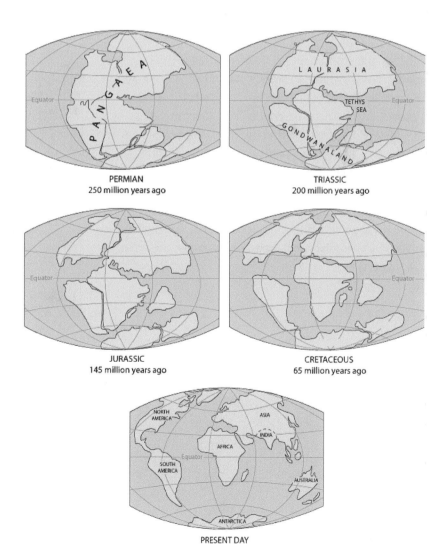

PERMIAN
250 million years ago

TRIASSIC
200 million years ago

JURASSIC
145 million years ago

CRETACEOUS
65 million years ago

PRESENT DAY

Image source: USGS

Pre-Lab Activity:
Searching for the Evidence of Drift

The Basics

The theory of plate tectonics is directly related to the continental drift hypothesis proposed by Alfred Wegener in 1915. He challenged ideas of the time that held that the continents had remained fixed in their position through all of Earth's history. He proposed that the continents at some point in their history, fit together like puzzle pieces into a vast supercontinent that he named Pangaea (Greek for all land). At the time, his hypothesis could not be proved to be correct. A mechanism that could result in the tremendous forces required to move a continent was lacking. This mechanism was later discovered and included in the plate tectonic theory developed in the 60's. The plate tectonic theory explains continental drift!

Begin Here

For this part of the lab, we will use a KML open use file created by geoscientists at James Madison University. Download and activate the pre-lab activity for "Lab 4 Plate Tectonics." Click "Help screen" inside the KML. It will help you navigate this complex file.

Image Source: Paulo Hidalgo

Lines of evidence explored in this Pre-Lab

Fit of the Continents

Mountain Belts

Fossil Evidence

Glacial Evidence

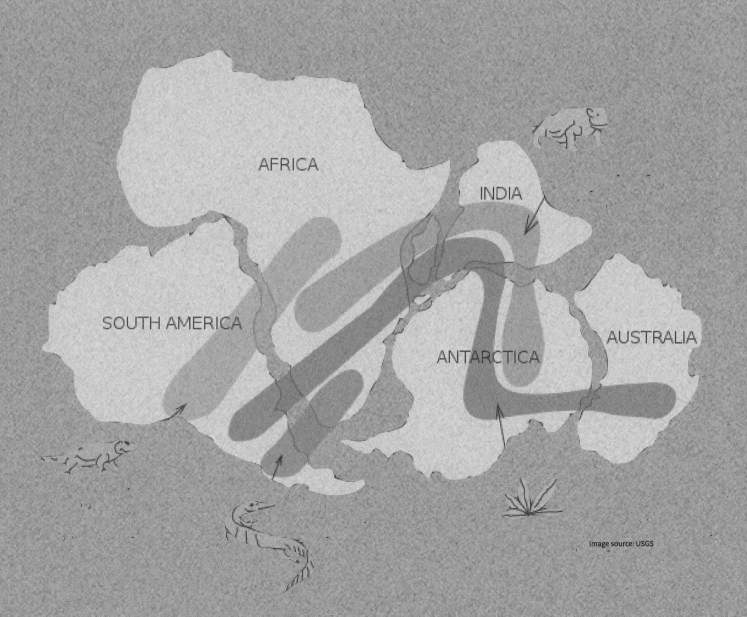

Image source: USGS

NOTES

==

 Alfred Wegener's (1880-1930) model of continental drift proposes that during the Mesozoic, a vast supercontinent that he named Pangea united most of the current continental masses on Earth today. He suggested that Pangea broke apart and gradually the continents drifted away to their current positions. Let's look at some of the lines of evidence that Wegener considered.

Pre-lab Activity

After following the instructions related to the KML file needed for this activity, you are ready to begin. You should see a view that looks a lot like the image on the previous page. Give it some time, there is a lot of information on this KML! After opening the KML, you will be able to time travel to 200 Ma (million years before present). At this time, Pangea was a sole massive supercontinent.

Step 1 - Geologic Time Indicator

200 Ma _____

The period in Ma for the continent arrangement displayed on the screen is in yellow colors in the upper right corner of the screen. .

Step 2- Time Travel

_____

You can fast forward or turn back in time by sliding the white tab on the blue bar at the top left corner of the window.

Step 3- Grid

_____

in Google Earth Pro, anytime that you need to see latitude and longitude lines all you have to do is click the "View" menu at the top of the google earth toolbar and then click on "grid."

Step 4- Continent Selection

_____

You can activate or deactivate continents by clicking the checkboxes in the places panel.

Step 5- Other features

_____

Other features of the KMZ such as fossil distribution and Paleozoic glaciation, can be activated or deactivated by checking the appropriate boxes.

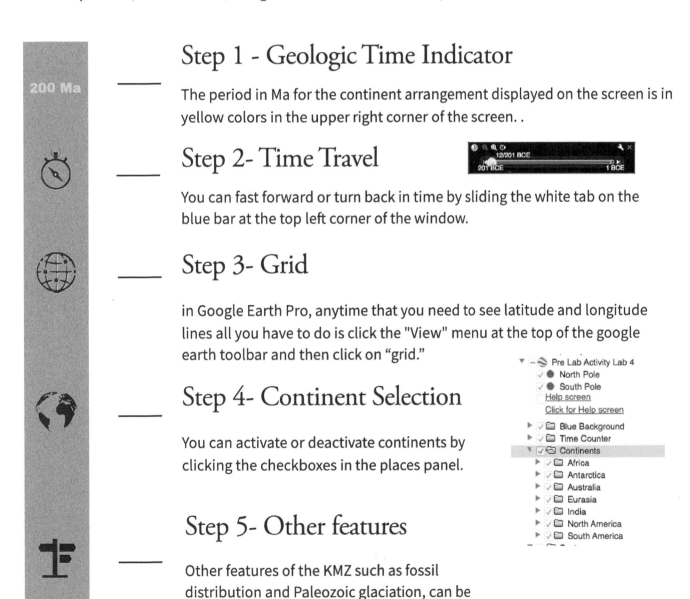

===

_____
Your Name

 From the moment that anybody looks at maps and globes of the world, one feature is apparent. The shape of the continents suggests to the imagination that continents could fit together like puzzle pieces. Wegener thought that this fit was too good to be coincidental.

1- 1- After you have explored the pre-lab KML, make yourself familiar with the location of the north and south poles and the current position of the continents. Now, go back 200 Ma by using the time travel slider. Which present day-continent was located at the North Pole? What continent was the closest to the South Pole? Hint: select and deselect continents under the "Continents" folder to get familiar with the specific colors that correspond to a given country.

North Pole:_____

South Pole:_____

2- Move forward to modern times. Find the Indian subcontinent and describe its movement from 200 Ma to modern times. Include connection, timing, and proximity to other land masses in your description.

_____

_____

_____

_____

3- In the last 100 Ma, which continent has moved the most? Which continent has moved the least?

_____

_____

 If the continents were joined together in Pangea, then in the connecting areas we should be able to see continuous or adjacent mountain belts. These are a product of continent-continent collision. Let's explore this hypothesis.

 Activate the "Mountain Belts" folder found under the "Features" folder which is found within the "Pre Lab" folder. Mountain ranges will appear in green.

🏔 4- Travel back in time to 200 Ma. Do you notice anything striking about the location of these mountain ranges? Were some of these mountain chains adjacent to each other? Which ones? Hint: if you zoom in towards the green symbols used for mountain ranges, the name of the range shows up.

_____

_____

_____

_____

🏔 5- The Himalayas make up the tallest chain of mountains in the world. These mountains separate the Indian subcontinent from the Tibetan Plateau. Use the KML file and move back and forward in time using the slider to determine how these mountains were formed and write your explanation in the following lines.

_____

_____

_____

_____

💡 Land-dwelling animals cannot swim across vast oceans. This is the reason why kangaroos and other marsupials live only in Australia. These mammals evolved independently and are only found there. In Pangea, all continents were joined together allowing migration of land animals across continents. Let's travel back to Pangea and using the fossil distribution that we find today, we should be able to distinguish which continental masses were connected at that time.

💬 *In the "Features" folder, deactivate "Mountain Belts" and activate the "Fossil Distribution" check box.*

🐚 6- Once again, travel through time to 200 Ma and list which continents were in proximity to each other based on fossil evidence. Expand the "Fossil distribution" tab to see the fossil names.

Using the Glossopteris geographic distribution, the following continents were together:

_____

Using the Mesosaurus geographic distribution, the following continents were together:

_____

Using the Lystrosaurus geographic distribution, the following continents were together:

_____

Using the Cynognathus geographic distribution, the following continents were together:

_____

⚙ 7- Does the fossil distribution make sense when combining it with the fit of continents? Explain.

_____

_____

💡 Wegener determined that the distribution of 200 Ma (Pangea's age) glacial sediments around the world is easily explained by the continents been united at that time. The southern part of Pangaea must have been the center of a massive ice cap.

💬 *In the "Features" folder, deactivate the "Fossil distribution" and activate the "Paleozoic Glaciations" check box.*

❄ 8- Not all continents were located at polar latitudes during Pangea's time (Paleozoic era). Which modern continents do not show evidence of glaciation during the Paleozoic? Which countries located away from polar latitudes today were once placed near the southern polar region?.

_____

_____

_____

_____

_____

❄ 9-Explain in a few sentences why your "continental drift denier" friend should change his/her/its mind.

_____

_____

_____

_____

_____

_____

_____

_____

NOTES

In-Lab Activity 1:
Landforms and Plate Tectonics

The Basics

The purpose of this lab is to teach you to recognize and interpret landform processes that are controlled by both active and ancient plate tectonic boundaries. Secondary objectives are related to understanding how plate tectonic boundaries influence landforms such as volcanoes, mountains, and deep-ocean trenches.

To fully understand this lab, you have to get acquainted with the following concepts:

Plate boundaries

- Transform, divergent, convergent boundaries
- Seafloor spreading and the determination of plate boundaries
- Hot Spots

Begin Here

Start by going into the plate tectonics lab in Google Earth Pro (click on the check box). Under the "In Lab Activity 1" folder, open the folder "Links to animations." Click on the links to access the animations, then answer the following questions.

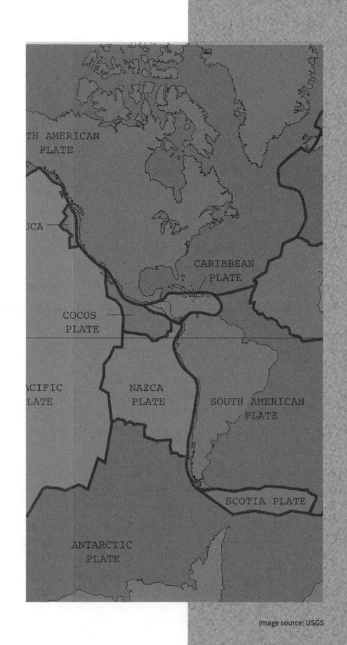

Image source: USGS

Topics explored in this section

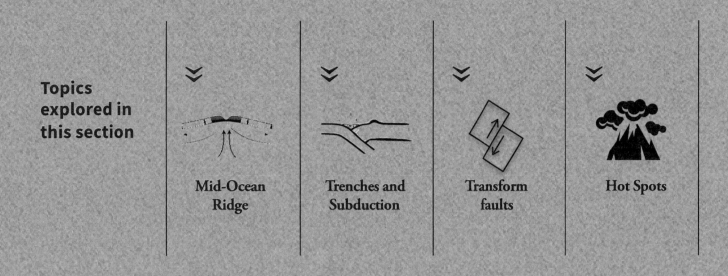

Mid-Ocean Ridge

Trenches and Subduction

Transform faults

Hot Spots

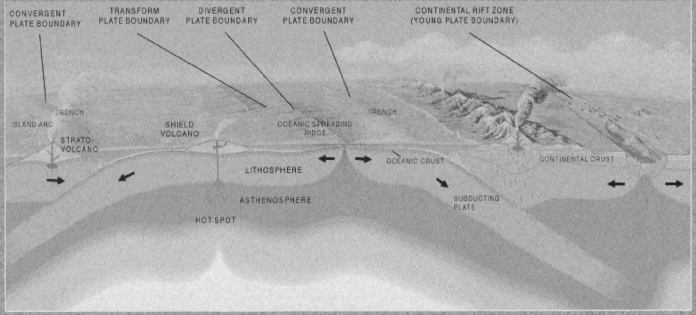

Image source: USGS

==

 # In-Lab Activity 1

Military needs during World War II helped in seafloor exploration. The sonar technology used allowed for the mapping of the seafloor. In the ocean, these maps are called bathymetric maps. In this section, you will discover some of the most striking topographical features in our oceans. Then we will use these features to explore the main concepts of this

1- Create a path from Savannah, Georgia to Dakhla, Oued Ed-Dahab-Lagouirau. Once your have created your path describe the topographical features that you see and how elevation changes along your path. Right-click on your path and click on "show elevation profile." Make sure your path is clamped to the seafloor (right-click, properties, altitude tab)

_____

_____

_____

_____

> The floor beneath major oceans includes abyssal plains, which are broad, relatively flat regions of the ocean that are found 4-5 km below sea level. Another feature of the seafloor is called a mid-ocean ridge. This is a submarine mountain range whose peaks lie 2-2.5 km below sea level.

2- Use the following box to recreate the topography that you discovered along your path and indicate if present the location of abyssal plains and mid-ocean ridges.

East
West

3- Using the ruler tool in the "path setting" try to determine approximately how long (in km) the mid-ocean ridge is in the Atlantic. In the south, it begins close to Antarctica, and in the north, it extends to latitudes that are close to the location of the geographic north pole. Use the wide fracture in the middle of the ridge as a guide.

Length: _____km

How amazing is to have this extremely long feature on the ocean floor!

HROV Nereus, a NOAA submersible that is used to study the deepest places on Earth was confirmed lost May 10, 2014. The vehicle was 10,000 meters deep when communication was lost. It is probable that the submersible imploded under pressure as great as 16,000 psi! Studying the ocean floor is hard!

Image source: NOAA

4- Still in the "In-Lab Activity 1," double click on "A". Create a path from A to B passing through the Challenger Deep. Clamp your path to seafloor. Once your have created your path describe the topographical features that you see and how elevation changes along your path.

_____
_____
_____
_____
_____

Along the perimeter of the Pacific Ocean, bathymetric studies have determined that the ocean floor reaches depths over 11,000 m deep. These geomorphological features are called "trenches." For reference, Mount Everest, the highest point on Earth is 8,848 m high.

5- Use the following box to recreate the topography that you discovered along your path and indicate if present, the location of abyssal plains, trenches and mid-ocean ridges.

West   East

The ocean floor is cut by narrow bands of vertical cracks called fracture zones. Most of these fracture zones lie at right angles to mid-ocean ridges. The ridge axis steps sideways (transform fault) when it intersects fracture zones.

6- Still in "Lab Activity 1" in Google Earth Pro, double click on "C". Using the ruler tool, determine approximately how long (in km) is the step between the mid-ocean ridge axes (distance from C to D).

Length: _____ km

NOTES

In-Lab Activity 2

Despite all the evidence that suggested that the Theory of Continental Drift prop by Wegener was right, it failed to be accepted by the scientific community. The reason was that Wegener failed to offer a mechanism for the movement of tremendously large continental masses across the surface of the Earth. In this section of the lab, you will learn about one of the most important discoveries in human history!

> *Under "In Lab Activity 2" in Google Earth Pro, activate "seafloor age map." Note: Make sure the "sediment thickness" folder beneath is deselected to avoid confusion.*

1- In the In-Lab Activity 1 question 3, you determined the length of the mid-ocean ridge in the Atlantic. This means that you know how to identify the crest of the mid-ocean ridge. Toggle on and off the "Seafloor age map." How does the age of the ocean floor correlate to the location of the mid-ocean ridge? Where are the oldest ages in the Atlantic seafloor found? What about the youngest?

_____

_____

_____

_____

_____

_____

> *Under "In-Lab Activity 2" in Google Earth Pro. Deactivate "Seafloor Age Map" and activate "sediment thickness."*

2-Sediments are found all over the ocean floor. These sediments are mostly composed of clay and tiny shells of plankton (like the ones on the image). How does the sediment thickness compare to the "seafloor age map"? Where are the thickest sediments? Close or away from the mid-ocean ridge? Explain.

©Videologia/shutterstock.com

_____

_____

_____

_____

===

Under "In-Lab Activity 2" in Google Earth Pro. Deactivate "Sediment thickness" and activate "Heat flux."

3- In the ocean floor, we have been able to measure the rate at which heat rises from its interior to the crust. We have realized that is not uniform. Use the Google Earth Pro to determine if there are specific locations where the heat flux is anomalously high. Explain your observations below.

_____

_____

_____

Under "In-Lab Activity 2" in Google Earth Pro, activate **ONLY** "Major Earthquakes" and "Plate Boundaries"

4- After you have activated the check boxes for "Major Earthquakes" and "Plate Boundaries," determine if the location of earthquakes is random or if there is some order. Does the location of the earthquakes follow bathymetric features that you described in previous sections of this lab? Explain.

_____

_____

_____

In the 1950s, a scientist named Harry Hess put together all the observations that you discovered in preceding sections of this lab and concluded that the high heat flow in mid-ocean ridges was related to the ascent of magma from great depths. These ridges matched the location of low magnitude earthquakes. He also proposed that the ocean floor sediments were thickest in places where the seafloor has deep depressions called trenches. This was the birth of the seafloor spreading theory that later became fundamental for the plate tectonics theory. **Click on the "seafloor spreading video."**

5- After watching the video, explain how crust forms along mid-ocean ridges and how this formation explains all the other observations (i.e. heat flow, earthquakes, seafloor age, etc).

_____

_____

_____

_____

_____

_____

_____

In-Lab Activity 3

Under "In-Lab Activity 3" in Google Earth Pro, watch the "Plate Tectonic Boundary video."

Q 1- Which plate tectonic boundary type produces new oceanic lithosphere (crust)? What is the evidence?

_____
_____
_____
_____

Q 2- Which boundary type does oceanic lithosphere ((crust) get destroyed? What is the evidence?

_____
_____
_____

THREE TYPES OF PLATE BOUNDARY

Divergent plate boundary — Ridge

Transform plate boundary — Earthquakes

Convergent plate boundary

©Designua/shutterstock.com

Click on the "Name of plates" box in "In-Lab Activity 3." Answer the following questions.

Q 3- What is the name of the plate the United States resides on?

_____

Q 4- Continental coasts can be the location where two or more tectonic plates meet (active margins). For example, go off-board of the west coast of the United States. Provide two other examples of plate boundaries that are on the coast of a country or continent.

_____
_____
_____
_____

Activate "seafloor age map" and click on the check boxes "A" and "B."

Q 5- Double-click on point "A." Use the measuring tool to measure (in kilometers) the distance between points "A" and "B." What is the distance?

_____

===

Q 6- Make sure to activate "Seafloor Age Map." Using the Seafloor Age legend on the top left of your screen, about how many million years ago (Ma) were these points once adjacent?

Q 7- Using the results of 5 and 6, calculate an approximate spreading rate in km/Ma and cm/yr for the mid-ocean Atlantic ridge. If the plates are moving apart symmetrically at the same rate (color bands are approximately equal), then dividing your answer by two will provide the average rate at which the South American Plate is moving west, and the African Plate is moving east.

_____

Q 8- Watch the animation titled "Himalayan Formation" and then use the box to draw a diagram that details: 1- What does this setting produce regarding landscapes or landscape features? 2- What are the names of the plates are involved? 3- What is the type of tectonic boundary?

West   East

Q 9- We have learned many concepts throughout this lab, and finally, you are capable of answering how plate tectonics influence the landscapes that we see in oceans and continents. Use the following lines to summarize the concepts that you learned.

_____
_____
_____
_____
_____
_____
_____

NOTES

©Bro Studio/shutterstock.com

EARTHQUAKES AND FAULTING

Objectives and Learning Outcomes

The intent of this lab exercise is to help transcend from observing simple textbook illustrations of crustal deformation processes and landforms to distinguishing and understanding these elements in real landscape sceneries. You will use Google Earth to view some specific locations that have folded or faulted landforms.

Ultimately, the purpose of this lab is to teach you to recognize and interpret landform processes that are caused by movement from earthquakes derived from induced stress. These earthquakes may be controlled by both active and ancient plate tectonic boundaries.

©Julian Frees/shutterstock.com

Destroyed houses in Kathmandu after the earthquake, April 2015. The event killed nearly 9,000 people and injured nearly 22,000.

©Antonio Nardelli/shutterstock.com

Amatrice - Rieti - Italy . An earthquake destroyed the city on April 28, 2016. It killed around 300 people and thousands were displaced.

©Sara_Escobar/shutterstock.com

Mexico City, September, 2017. After a 7.1 earthquake, Mexico City inhabitants went to the streets to help to rescue those persons caught in the collapsed buildings.

©Arimdambanerjee/shutterstock.com

Port Au Prince, Haiti- August 28, 2010: A Valley of broken houses and debris after a 7.0 magnitude earthquake. 92000 people were killed.

©OBJM/shutterstock.com

Reality of the tsunami disaster of the aftermath of the 2011 Tohoku earthquake and tsunami.

Image source: NOAA

Image shows radioactive seepage spreading across the Pacific Ocean from the Fukushima nuclear plant.

NOTES

_____

Your Name

Earthquakes and Landforms

> *Bedrock is very resilient and can withstand tremendous amounts of stress, but not endlessly. Tectonic forces acting on bedrock can cause deformation and ultimately break or rupture the rocks creating earthquakes. Faults are fractures in bedrock along which movement has occurred. Faults are weak areas and therefore susceptible to further rupturing. Prolonged deformation has an important impact on the evolution of the Earth's landscapes.*

> *Expand the folder "Pre-Lab" in the "Earthquakes Lab" in Google Earth. You will double-click on "Deformation Figure 1a" and then answer questions associated with the figure in the designated area.*

Pre-lab Activity

1- Explain what is the difference between ductile deformation and fragile deformation and how they may influence the superficial landforms that we observe.

_____
_____
_____
_____
_____

> *Double-click at "Deformation Figure 1b." The figure consists of three parts: (a) Tensional stress, (b) compressional stress, and (c) shear stress. After studying over the figure, uncheck "Deformation Figure."*

2-Click and match each of "Place 1, Place 2, and Place 3" landscapes with the (a), (b), and (c) parts of the figure. Make sure you pay attention to the arrows in these figures.

Place 1: _____, Reasoning:_____
Place 2: _____, Reasoning:_____
Place 3: _____, Reasoning:_____

3- In the "Deformation Figure 1c" you are presented with a series of fault diagrams. In all of them, the direction of the stress is indicated. What is the difference between normal and reverse (or thrust faults) faults concerning the direction of the stress and the movement of the hanging wall (against or in favor of gravity)?

_____

_____

_____

_____

_____

_____

Double-click on the "Place 1" folder, make sure box is activated.

4- "Place 1" shows the Grand Tetons fault (in yellow), which is a (normal, reverse, strike slip) _____fault. Because of this reason the right side of the fault is moving up or down? _____ Compare this image to the Deformation Figure 1c and provide a couple of lines of evidence to support your answer. (It may be useful to right-click on the "topographic profile line" in this folder in the sidebar to create an elevation profile.)

These are the Grand Tetons in western Wyoming, USA. They are a product of extension and thinning of the North American Plate.

Enter your answer to question 4 here:

_____

_____

_____

_____

_____

==

Double-click on the "Place 2" folder, make sure box is activated.

5- Because of the type of stresses involved in "Place 2," the Caucasus Mountains may present (normal, reverse, strike-slip) _____faults. Compare this image to the Deformation Figure 1c and provide a couple of lines of evidence to support your answer. (It may be useful to right-click on the topographic profile line in the sidebar to create an elevation profile.)

The Caucasus Mountains are located on the boundary between 4 countries: Russia, Georgia, Armenia, and Azerbaijan. They formed mainly due to the collision of two continental plates (Arabian and Eurasian).

Enter your answer to question 5 here:

_____

_____

_____

Double-click on the "Place 3" folder, make sure box is activated.

6- Because of the type of stresses involved in "Place 3," the San Andreas Fault may present what type of (normal, reverse, strike-slip) _____fault? Compare this image to the Deformation Figure 1c and provide a couple of lines of evidence to support your answer. (It may be useful to see if there are displacements along streams.)

The San Andreas Fault is perhaps the most famous fault in the world. Is located in California where two tectonic plates touch, the North American, and the Pacific Plates.

Enter your answer to question 6 here:

_____

_____

NOTES

Seismic Waves

 During the breaking, energy is released as seismic waves that behave similarly to sound waves. Just like sound waves, the velocity of seismic waves is dependent on the medium it passes through. In this section, you will be watching animations and understanding the basic landforms associated with crustal movement and earthquakes.

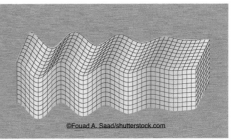

©Fouad A. Saad/shutterstock.com

Activate "In-Lab activity 1" and expand the "Question 1" folder. Activate the "Salt Lake" folder and double-click on it. Click on the link that appears when you click the salt lake icon in the map screen. After watching the animation go back to Google Earth and answer the following questions about the location.

🧪 In-Lab Activity 1

1-What is the behavior of seismic waves as they pass through dense rock? What about a medium of softer sediment?

_____

_____

_____

_____

_____

In the "In-Lab Activity 1" folder open the "Question 2 folder" and double click on "Deformation Figure 1b." The figure consists of three parts: (a) Tensional stress, (b) compressional stress, and (c) shear stress. After studying over the figure, uncheck the *"Deformation Figure."*

2-During the amplification animation, what happens to the energy waves as they pass through the valley and reach the mountain? What type of material you expect to find in valleys?

_____

_____

_____

_____

===

Let's see a practical example of these concepts. Still in "In-Lab activity 1"" expand the "question 3" folder. Look at both of the images and their description and then answer the following

3-Mexico City is a hot spot for earthquakes because vast chunks of the earth's crust (tectonic plates), are slowly smashing into one another nearby. However, the devastation produced by earthquakes in this region is many times larger than should be expected under normal conditions. How can the diagrams in the "question 3 folder" be used to explain the destruction that Mexico City has faced in the last two large seismic events in 1985 and 2017?

_____
_____
_____
_____
_____

4-Back on Google Earth, "Question 1" folder. Which areas in the "Earthquake (EQ) Polygon" will you rather be during an earthquake when taking into account ground shaking as the seismic waves travel from the earthquake's location (marked by the symbol) outward to the mountain range to the west? Will you rather be in the mountains? Or in a lake house? Explain why?

_____
_____
_____
_____

Check the "Horst and Graben" box in the "Question 1" folder. Click on each of the numbers and watch the animations. Go back to Google Earth and answer the following questions. The location of the numbers is not directly associated with the animations.

5-Explain the motion of crustal masses that is observed during a normal fault.

_____
_____
_____

6-What landscape evidence may be indicative of a normal fault?

_____
_____
_____

7-What similarities can you find between a thrust fault and a normal fault in terms of landscape modification?

_____

_____

_____

8-What is Horst and Graben topography and how is it formed? (You may click on "Figure 2.1" in the "In-lab Activity 1" folder to get some help.)

_____

_____

_____

9-When comparing what you see in "Figure 2.1" with the topography presented in locations 1 to 3, which area represents the Graben (1, 2, 3)? Explain.

_____

_____

_____

10-Based on your previous answer, which location(s) is less susceptible to ground shaking? Which number(s) is more susceptible to ground shaking? Explain.

_____

_____

_____

Tectonics and Earthquakes

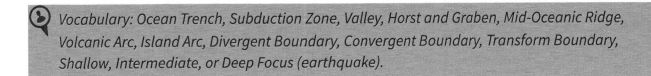

The distribution of earthquakes across the globe has helped us come a long way in the study of plate tectonics. There are earthquakes at every plate boundary where stress builds up over time and results in crustal shortening or thickening. Now you will be going to various locations in Google Earth to describe the distribution of earthquakes and the tectonic environments that are responsible for faulting. Below are some vocabulary terms that can help you in your

Vocabulary: Ocean Trench, Subduction Zone, Valley, Horst and Graben, Mid-Oceanic Ridge, Volcanic Arc, Island Arc, Divergent Boundary, Convergent Boundary, Transform Boundary, Shallow, Intermediate, or Deep Focus (earthquake).

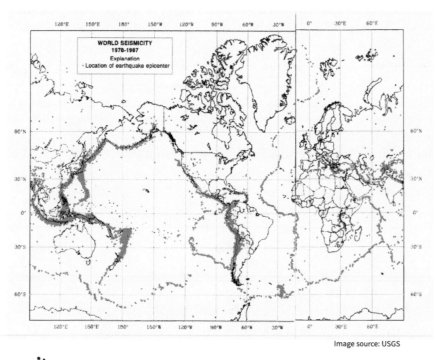

Image source: USGS

Ninety percent of the world's earthquakes occur in specific areas that are the boundaries of the Earth's major crustal plates.

🧪 In-Lab Activity 2

 Open the "In-Lab activity 2" folder. *Click on the "Mid-Atlantic Ridge" photo. The stars indicate epicenters of earthquakes at the boundary (you can zoom in).*

1-What kind of plate tectonics boundary does the image represent (pay attention to the arrows)? What is the evidence?

_____

_____

2-What fault (s) type is responsible for creating this boundary? (Pay attention to the arrows and to any displacements.)

_____

_____

_____

 Click on the "Convergent Margin" photo. This will take you to a new location on the west coast of South America. The small star-shaped figures represent earthquake hypocenter locations in the plates.

===

3-What fault types do you see in this setting? What is the evidence? Remember that in the figure, the faults are the little thin lines in the shallow crust and that this tectonic environment is controlled by compressional forces.

_____

_____

_____

_____

4-Theorize about what landforms are produced as a result of this tectonic boundary? (Give examples in by referring to the names of these landforms in South America or Asia.)

_____

_____

_____

_____

5-What aspect about earthquakes (intensity, magnitude, depth, etc.) will you use to differentiate between convergent or divergent tectonic boundaries? Explain.

_____

_____

_____

_____

Click on the "Continental Settings of EQs" photo. The earthquake locations are represented by red dots.

6-How does the distribution of earthquakes relate to the areas of greatest deformation (i.e. more landscape modification)?

_____

_____

_____

_____

7-What predictions can you make in terms of landscape elevation if the region remains active? (Hint: Look at the arrows.)

_____

_____

_____

_____

Check the "United States Geological Survey (USGS) Earthquakes" and the "Earth's Tectonic Plates" boxes to see a global distribution of earthquakes (in the past 60 years) color-coded by depth, and the magnitude is designated as size of the circle.

==

8-What do you notice about the worldwide distribution of earthquakes? Is there any correlation with the plate tectonic overlay?

_____

_____

_____

9-Where do you expect the landscape to be modified the most, away or close to these earthquake belts? Provide examples with your answer using South America's landforms.

_____

_____

_____

10-Take a look at the west coast of South America. Where are the shallow earthquakes distributed? Close, far from a plate boundary? What about the earthquakes with a greater depth? How can this be? (Hint: The "Convergent Margin" image may contain the answer.)

_____

_____

11-Draw an "earthquake depth" versus "distance from coast" graph that illustrates the data earthquake variation in this polygon. (Activate the red line in the "Line" folder found in the "in-lab activity 2" folder. It is included as a guide in Google Earth Pro.)

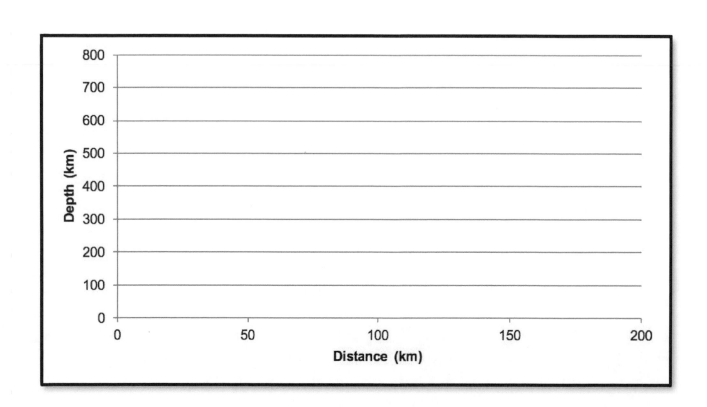

===

Fault zones may not be as apparent as the San Andreas Fault. In some, lakes may form specially if the fault zone comes in contact with the water table. These lakes are known as rift lakes or sag ponds, forming in a region of low topography created by the fault movement.

Click on the "Lake Baikal" box in "In-Lab Activity 2." Double-click to make sure you travel to the location.

12-Provide an explanation on how the water might have collected there to form Lake Baikal. (Hint: This area is under tensional stress.)

_____

_____

_____

Click on the "Red Sea" box in "In-Lab Activity 2" folder. Double-click to make sure you travel to the location.

13-What kind of plate boundary is this environment based on the topography that you observe in addition to the presence of water?

_____

_____

14-Speculators speculate. How was the Red Sea formed? What will be the future of the land north of Suez (Activate "Suez polygon")?

_____

_____

_____

_____

15-Summarize how earthquakes and stress modify the landscape around and indicate in what regions of the Earth landscape evolution is more active.

_____

_____

_____

_____

_____

_____

NOTES

NOTES

©bigredlynx/shutterstock.com

FLUVIAL LANDFORMS

6

The Work of Stream Systems

Streams and channels are responsible for most of the superficial landform shaping. The work of streams begins with the erosion and transport of sediments and ions, but they also may deposit sediments creating new landforms. The discipline that studies the formation of landscapes is called fluvial geomorphology.

Streams are an essential part of the Earth system

Streams transport water and sediment from discrete regions known as drainage basins or watersheds. The quantity of water and sediment in a basin is contingent on factors such as the amount of precipitation, the erodibility of soil, and the dimensions of the basin. These factors are not consistent from place to place, and therefore, there are dissimilarities in processes and morphology from one stream to another. Some streams flow on or very close to bedrock.

These bedrock channels are usually quite steep and have little opportunity to build fluvial landforms. Other rivers, termed alluvial rivers, flow over fluvial sediment, or alluvium, and have a superior ability to transform their channel and create floodplains and other fluvial landforms. This lab focuses and gives you the tools to identify these landscapes and predict their evolution.

©Naeblys/shutterstock.com

source: Paulo Hidalgo

Grand Canyon of Yellowstone

source: Paulo Hidalgo

Glacial lake in Alberta, Canada

©Serg Zastavkin/shutterstock.com

Tundra Landscapes, North Yakutia

The water cycle

If the Earth's surface were flat, the great diversity of landscapes that adorn our sights would not exist. The Earth is not flat due to the combination of two of the Earth's most potent processes. Plate Tectonics that uplifts and creates mountains and valleys, and the hydrologic cycle where water in all its forms being water, ice, or water vapor modifies the landscapes by erosion and transport of sediment from the highlands to the low lying ocean floor.

NOTES

==

Your Name

 # Pre-Lab Activity

1- The hydrologic cycle plays an integral role in shaping the land. Look at the figure below describing the hydrologic cycle. What are the three ways that water goes back into the atmosphere? Where does most of the water in the atmosphere come from?

_____

_____

_____

_____

_____

_____

_____

_____

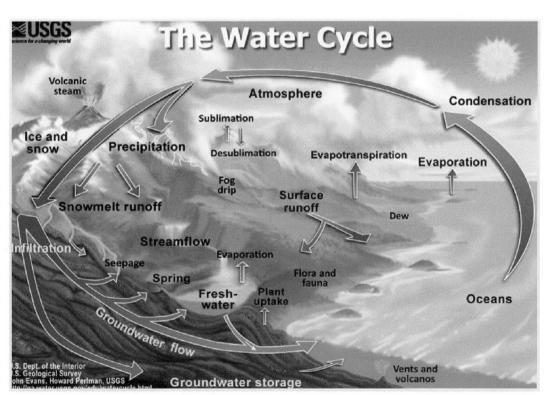

source: USGS

Open folder "Pre-Lab Activity". Click on "Continental Divides of North America."

===

2- You will now see the divides of North America. These divides are places where the major drainage basins meet. Notice that one of them cuts through the middle of a major southern city (one that you may be familiar with). If rain were to fall at point 1, in what major water body would it end up? Why? (Hint: Activate "US Major Rivers" in the "Prelab Activity" folder.)

_____

_____

_____

_____

3- Water that flows on the surface is called surface water. It collects and flows as streams and rivers. Many of these rivers have different patterns. Look at the picture by double clicking on "Question 3" and notice the different types of patterns. Identify the types of river patterns of points 2 and 3. Notice that not all of the types of drainage patterns will be used.

_____

_____

_____

_____

4- Some streams do not always have water. These streams are ephemeral streams. Why do these streams exist? When would they contain water? In what type of climate are they likely to be found?

_____

_____

_____

_____

_____

The amount of water that flows in a river or stream is measured by discharge. Discharge is calculated using the equation below:

$$Q = A_c \times V_a$$

A_c=is the cross-sectional area of the stream which will be measured in squared units (m2 or ft2).
V_a=is the velocity of the flow and is measured by distance over time (m/second, ft/minute).
Q=is the discharge of the stream and is measured in cubic units over time (m3/minute, ft3/second).

In the folder "Pre-Lab Activity", double-click on point 5.

==

5- Measure the width of the Chattahoochee River at point 5. Calculate the stream discharge assuming an average depth of 4 ft and a flow of 7 ft/second. Show your calculations here.

6- Measure the width of the Mississippi River at point 6. Calculate the stream discharge assuming an average depth of 7 ft and a flow of 1.7 ft/second. Show your calculations here.

7- Measure the width of the Amazon River at point 7. Calculate the stream discharge assuming an average depth of 170 ft and a flow of 14 ft/second. Show your calculations here.

8- Which stream has a greater discharge? Why is the discharge of this river so much higher than the other two?

_____
_____
_____
_____
_____
_____

NOTES

===

Drainage patterns

Your Name

Over time, river channels combine with smaller tributaries joining a larger trunk stream. The associated channels become what is known as a drainage network. Drainages tend to mature along zones where rock type and structure are most easily eroded. Thus these drainage patterns reflect the structure of the rock. For example, dendritic drainage develops on a surface where the underlying rock has uniform resistance to erosion, radial drainages form in areas of high topography where elevation drops from a central high area to surrounding low areas, and rectangular drainage patterns develop at linear zones of weakness. In this section, we will explore drainage patterns in its link to landscapes.

In this section we will explore the morphology of streams and drainage systems. Open "In-Lab Activity 1" folder.

In-Lab Activity 1

 1-Identify the types of stream channel and match them to the locations given in points 1 to 3 inside the "In-Lab Activity 1" folder and explain how they formed.

Straight_____

_____M

eandering_____

_____B

raided_____

Straight stream channels are uncommon. When it happens, the channel is usually coordinated by a linear zone of weakness in the underlying bedrock, like a fault or joint system. Because of the velocity configuration of a stream, straight channels will ultimately erode into meandering channels. In streams that have a wide variability in discharge and have easily eroded banks, sediment gets dropped to form bars and islands that are uncovered during phases of low discharge. In such a stream, the water flows in a braided pattern around the islands and bars. Such a channel is termed a braided channel.

©Byelikova Oksana/shutterstock.com

==

2-Meandering rivers have many landforms associated with them. Match the locations of points 1 to 7 inside the "Question 2 folder" with the name of the landform and explain how they are created.

Cut Bank_____

Point Bar_____

Oxbow lake _____

Yazoo Stream_____

Cut-off_____

Meander Neck_____

Flood Plain_____

3-Discuss the processes of deposition and erosion that are active in the area displayed in "P" inside "In-Lab Activity 1" folder and make a drawing of the sequence of processes that lead to the formation of the Oxbow lake (crescent shape tree area to the south of Point 3). (Hint: Click on Figure 2.4 to get more information).

_____
_____
_____
_____

4-Navigate to point 4 and note the elevation of the lake at that point. This lake is at local base level. What is the name of this lake? How was this lake formed and how far above the ultimate base level is it?

_____
_____
_____
_____
_____
_____
_____
_____

5-As uplift occurs, rivers can cut into rocks at a great rate. What landform was created by the uplift at point 5? What river has cut into that landform to create the canyon you see?

_____

_____

_____

6- Some geologists are finding evidence that suggests that this mile deep canyon may have been cut with the last 4 million years. Assuming a uniform rate of erosion and without considering canyon widening due to slop retreat, calculate how much (in millimeters per year) the Colorado River would have to downcut per year to form this mile-deep canyon in 4 million years. Show your work and clearly indicate what each quantity represents.

6-What type of canyon is the canyon at point 6? How can you tell? Read through the text in the Google Earth Pro point 6 link to learn more about canyon types.

_____

_____

_____

_____

7-Navigate to point 7. How many terraces can you identify? What is the elevation of each terrace? Approximately how wide is the oldest terrace?

Number of Terraces: _____

Elevation of terraces (one value for each): _____

Width of the oldest terrace:_____

8-Name the feature identified by point 8. How and why is this landform similar to a delta? Is this an erosional or depositional environment?

_____

_____

_____

_____

9-What type of drainage pattern is at point 9? How is it different from other ones in the lab? Include a simple sketch of the drainage pattern and explain why this type of drainage pattern is observed here.

_____

_____

_____

11-What type of feature is the area around point 10? Draw a sketch of this feature.

_____

In-Lab Activity 2

Headward erosion is the removal of material at the origin of a stream channel, which causes the head of the stream to move back away from the direction of the stream flow, and so creates the stream channel to lengthen.

In this section we will explore processes that modify the stream morphology. Open "In-Lab Activity 2" folder.

1- Go to Canyonlands National Park in Utah, USA. Look at the geomorphology of the park and indicate using coordinates three examples of headward erosion and it what direction the stream is lengthening (north, south, east, west).

Location 1_____

Location 2_____

Location 3_____

2-A farmer has proposed to you a fabulous farmland deal in South Dakota neighboring the Badlands National Park. Click on "Point 2" in "In-Lab Activity 2" folder to see its location. Would you buy this land? Why?

_____

_____

_____

===

3-Click on Placemark 3, it will take you to _____(name of the river and country of location). Watch the video about meanders. Write an explanation for the developing of the copious meanders found in the floodplain of this river.

_____

_____

_____

_____

_____

_____

4- Check and double-click placemark 4. Now you are traveling to Moab, Utah. You are looking at an area surrounding the incised meander system of the Green River called Bowknot Bend. The old abandoned meander that you see was cut off sometime in the past and now has been bypassed by the Green River. This is why it does not have water. Did the cutoff happen before or after the river incised/entrenched into the landscape? Explain.

_____

_____

_____

_____

5-In the "In-Lab Activity 2" folder, click on "Question 5" folder and then on "Young," "Mature" and "Old". Explore all the images and read their descriptions. Describe the changes that a stream experiences from young to old and the causes of these changes.

_____

_____

_____

_____

_____

_____

Navigate to Mars, the 4th planet from the Sun (~101 million miles from Earth). You may do this by clicking on the planet icon (6th icon from the right, at the top of the Google Earth window) and selecting Mars. You have now been whisked away to Mars! How exciting (and dusty)!

You have learned quite a lot throughout this lab, now you are finally ready to make your own discoveries in another terrestrial planet!

©Jurik Peter/shutterstock.com

In-Lab Activity 3

1- Go to point 3.1 in the "In-Lab Activity 3" folder. Describe the linear features that are radiating from one of the flanks of the volcano. If you decide that the evidence indicates that these are in fact stream channels, what type of drainage is present? What is the evidence? Include an illustration of that drainage pattern.

_____

_____

_____

2-Still in point 3.1, what does this pattern tell you about the underlying material? Is it homogeneous or heterogeneous? Is this material easily erodible? (Think back to part 1 of this lab.)

_____

_____

_____

3- Go to point 3.2. The area at point 2 is called Warrego Valles. Identify and draw a sketch of the drainage pattern that you see. How were these valleys formed?

_____

_____

_____

==

4- Navigate to point 3. Notice the stream system at the northeast rim of the crater. Describe the valley below this point. Draw a sketch of this valley system and label the areas of erosion and deposition. How do you know that these areas are erosional or depositional?

_____

_____

_____

_____

5- A) Navigate to point 3.4. This area is known as Noctis Labyrinthus and is on the western edge of Vallis Marineris, the "Grand Canyon of Mars." Assume that water has flowed through this area: what type of drainage pattern is present here? Include a simple sketch of the drainage pattern below. What does this type of drainage pattern suggest about the underlying bedrock?

_____

_____

B) Last, scan to the East: if water did flow through Noctis Labyrinthus, where did that water end up? Suggest some possible place/feature names – you might also wish to explore the Colorized Terrain layers for elevation information (in layers panel, expand the Global Maps folder and activate Colorized terrain).

_____

_____

_____

==

6- Navigate to point 3.5. This area is in an area called the Eberswalde. Sketch and identify the landform in this area. It has recently been chosen as a landing site for the Mars Laboratory Mission. Why would this be a good landing site?

_____

_____

_____

7- The image to the left is an alluvial fan caused by the Lawn Lake Flood in the Endovalley, Rocky Mountain National Park, Colorado. The picture on the right was taken by Nasa's Mars Global Surveyor (MGS) Mars Orbiter Camera (MOC). How can you use these images to find evidence to support the presence of water on Mars?

©Vagabond54/shutterstock.com

440 yd
400 m
source: NASA

_____

_____

_____

_____

_____

_____

_____

NOTES

©ma.petite.planete/shutterstock.com

ARID LANDFORMS

7

"What makes the desert beautiful
is that somewhere it hides a well."

Antoine de Saint-Exupéry

The extremely low precipitation causes arid landscapes to appear quite unlike those of other climatic circumstances. The restricted water supply limits rock weathering as well as the area of vegetation present. Without extensive vegetation to hold weathered rock (regolith) in place, the weathered rock bits are habitually exposed away when storms occur. As a result, hill slopes in humid regions tend to be rounded and mantled by soil and mountains and hill slopes in arid regions are generally angular, with extensive barren exposures of bedrock. Arid valleys may be filled in with sediments eroded from uplands, or they may comprise a thin cover of sediments overlying rock. This lab will give you a quick overlook of the landscapes that are observed in arid environments.

source: Paulo Hidalgo

Your guide to this lab

source: Paulo Hidalgo

Main Objective

The purpose of this lab is to familiarize you, the student, with desert types, desert landforms, and the processes that craft them. Secondary objectives include exploring societal elements in deserts and the process of desertification in temperate landscapes.

source: Paulo Hidalgo

Other Objectives

• Be able to identify the different types of deserts
• Effectively identify the different types of landforms in deserts
• Understand the role of fluvial and Eolian processes in shaping the deserts
• Recognize the impacts of desertification

source: Paulo Hidalgo

Core Concepts

• In most deserts, running water is scarce, however this process is so important in shaping the landscape in arid areas.
• In most regions on Earth, wind is not an important factor when discussing landform development. However, under certain circumstances it can be an important geomorphologic agent.

NOTES

===

🧪 Pre-Lab Activity————————————

Your Name

> 💡 *In temperate and humid regions, plant cover protects the ground surface from the wind, but in deserts, the wind has direct access to the ground. Wind, just like flowing water, can carry sediment both as suspended load and as surface load. It is by this process that a dune is created. A dune is an accumulation of sand deposited by a moving current. Dunes can be of a variety of shapes and sizes depending on the wind strength, wind direction, and availability of sand.*

> 💬 *Open folder "Pre-Lab Activity". Click on the "Terms" link under to be taken to a website with definitions, diagrams, and illustrations. Use the website to answer the following questions.*

1- Double-click on "Q1 Dune." Notice if there are radiating arms or "horns" on these dunes in the _____(name of desert) in the country of_____. Which type of dune is seen at this location? What, if any, is the predominant wind direction at this location?

_____

_____

_____

_____

2-Double-click on "Q2 Dune." Notice if there are "horns" or radiating arms on these dunes located in the _____(name of desert) in the country of_____. Which type of dune is seen at this location? What is the predominant wind direction at this location?

_____

_____

_____

_____

3-Indicate the average wind direction by drawing an arrow on the diagram below. The rock in the picture is a ventifact. Is the process that shaped this rock fluvial or Eolian? Describe why this rock is shaped the way it is.

source: Paulo Hidalgo

===

Double-click on "Q4 Up Close" under "Pre-Lab Activity."

4- This photo was taken in the _____(name of desert) in the country
of_____; a very windy location. Observe the rocky groundcover. What type
of desert landform is this? Describe the role of wind in the formation of this landscape.

_____

_____

_____

_____

5-You and your pet squirrel are enjoying the breathtaking scenery of Arches National Park, Utah.
Stacey, your squirrel, wants to know how the rugged landforms called buttes formed. Explain the
process of differential weathering to Stacey.

_____

_____

_____

_____

source: Paulo Hidalgo

Double-click on "Q6 Landform" under "Part 1." Click on "Up Close" to see a detailed photo.

6-These fan-shaped deposits located in_____ are landforms that develop
at the base of a hill where flow velocity has decreased to a degree that sediment is deposited.
What type of landform is this? How is it similar or different from the one in the picture below?

_____

_____

_____

_____

source: Paulo Hidalgo

===

7- Contrast the type of weathering found in arid regions compared with the one located in tropical areas. What kinds of chemical weathering or mechanical weathering are found in arid regions?

_____

_____

_____

_____

_____

Double-click on "Q8 Landform."

8-The red sandstone of Uluru (Ayers Rock), a bornhardt, rises above the stony plains of the central Australian desert. The NW-trending diagonal lines are traces of vertical bedding in the sandstone. Why is this sandstone rock a positive feature prominent in the surrounding flat landscape?

_____

_____

_____

_____

Double-click on "Q9 Landform."

9-Huge dunes of orange sand border a dry wash in western Africa. The slip faces of dunes are recognizable. A road in the wash provides scale. Describe the physical processes responsible for this landscape (i.e. fluvial, eolian, tectonic, etc)?

_____

_____

_____

_____

Double-click on "Q10 Landform."

10-Fly to "Q10 landform". The Egyptian civilization is one of the oldest in the world. Access to water is extremely vital to human settlements, and this millenarian culture made sure to have regular access to an abundant water supply. Zoom out to an "eye altitude" of 480 km What is the middle of the green area in the center of your view? What is the name of the vast arid region around it? Why does the green area have a triangular shape near the ocean?

_____

_____

_____

_____

_____

_____

NOTES

In-Lab Activity 1

Your Name

There are unique vegetational and landscape features that distinguish one desert from another. Geoscientists have classified deserts based on the environment and the processes that formed them. There are five types of deserts: subtropical, rain shadow, cold coastal current, interior of continents, and polar region deserts. Click on the link inside "In-Lab Activity 1" for more information.

Open folder "Question 1" in "In-Lab Activity 1". Study the diagrams separately first and then together. Use the pictures to answer the following question.

1- When we look at annual rainfall patterns in"Picture 2" is clear that there are areas in the world that receive less than average amounts of precipitation. Oddly, these areas are equidistantly and symmetrically located north and south of the equator. Use "Picture 1" 1 to explain this distribution.

_____

_____

_____

_____

_____

_____

_____

You will be working under "Question 2" for this portion of the exercise. Continue using the website for help answering the following questions. Double-click on "Taklimakan Desert." Click on "Up Close" to see a more detailed photo.

2-The Taklimakan Desert in northwest China is bounded by five mountain ranges; the Altuns to the Southeast, the Kunlun Mountains to the South, the Karakoram to the Southwest, the Pamirs to the West, and the Tian Shan Mountains to the North. These mountain ranges are indicated by the green polygons. Answer the following questions:
Type of desert:_____

a)Measure the change in elevation (in meters) from the Central Karakoram National Park (K2) to the CENTER of the Taklimakan Desert. Place your cursor on the different locations and read the corresponding elevation in the bottom right corner of the Google Earth window. If you cannot see the numbers you will need to collapse the 'tour guide' feature along the bottom of the window. Alternatively, you can use the purple line to see a detailed elevation profile and get this number.

Change in Elevation (m):_____

==

b) What happens to humid air masses upon reaching a mountain range?

_____

_____

c) What happens to the water contained in rising/cooling air?

_____

_____

d) What becomes the inland side of the mountain range?

_____

_____

> *Double-click on "Namib Desert" under "Question 3". Click on "Up Close" to see a more detailed photo.*

3-The Namib Desert extends over 1,200 miles along the Atlantic coast of Africa through Angola, Namibia, and South Africa. The aridity of the Namib is owed to the Benguela Current along the Atlantic African coast. Activate the sea surface temperature to see what type of current is this (hot or cold) . Answer the following questions:

Type of desert:_____

Compared to other deserts, the Namib is very narrow. Use the ruler at the top of the Google Earth window to measure the distance, in kilometers, along the yellow line from the Namib Desert coast to its eastern border.

Namib width (km): _____

> *Double-click on "Peary Land, Greenland" under "Question 4". Click on "Up Close" to see a detailed photo. Deactivate the surface temperature layer*

4- Peary Land is a peninsula in Northern Greenland that extends into the Arctic Ocean. At first glance, Peary Land may not look like a desert, however, it receives under 20 cm of rain per year.

Type of desert:_____

a) Use the ruler tool at the top of the Google Earth window to measure the distance, in kilometers, along with the yellow line from Peary Land to the North Pole.

Distance (km): _____

==

b) Pull down the view menu at the top of the Google Earth window and select the 'grid' feature to see lines of latitude and longitude. What is the latitude at the Peary Land placemark and in the North Pole?

Peary Land Latitude_____

North Pole Latitude_____

> Double-click on "Gobi Desert" under "Question 5." Click on "Up Close" to see a detailed photo.

5-The Gobi Desert straddles northern China and southern Mongolia in the heart of Asia. Use the ruler tool to measure the distance, in kilometers, along the yellow line from the Gobi Desert placemark to the Yellow Sea.

a) Type of Desert:_____

Distance:_____

b)Click on the "Up Close" photo. Observe the tightly packed concentration of large pebbles in the foreground. What type of landform is this?

_____

> Double-click on "Sahara Desert" under "Question 6". Click on "Up Close" to see a detailed photo

6- The Sahara of Northern Africa is the third largest desert in the world. The Sahara Desert is centered on the Tropic of Cancer. Reactivate the 'grid' feature. At roughly what latitude does the Sahara terminate along its southern border?

Type of Desert:

a)Latitude:_____

b)At roughly what latitude does the Sahara terminate into the Mediterranean Sea?

Latitude:

_____

c)Click on the "Up Close" photo. Observe the resistant layers of rock that protect the weaker underlying rock. What type of weathering results in landforms like these?

_____

In-Lab Activity 2

The shrinking of the Aral Sea is widely considered to be one of the worst environmental disasters in history. The surface area of the lake before 1960 was 68,000 km². In the 1960's, a Soviet irrigation project led to the diversion of the two rivers that fed into the Aral Sea. Not surprisingly, the Aral Sea has been steadily shrinking ever since. The impact has been profound and far-reaching. The once-robust fishing industry has collapsed, leaving tens of thousands unemployed. Huge salt-covered plains produce choking sandstorms. The massive loss of water has even changed local climate- summers are now hotter and drier, and winters are longer and colder.

You will be working under "In-Lab Activity 2" for this portion of the lab.
Double-click on "Aral Sea, Kazakhstan," under the "Question 1" folder. Expand the folder and check only the box indicating 1973. One by one check each box and observe the rapidly shrinking

1-a) What is the area, in square kilometers, of the Aral Sea in 1973? Repeat this for the other years.

_____

1986 Surface Area: _____

1999 Surface Area: _____

2004 Surface Area: _____

b) What is the difference in surface area from 1973 to 2004?

_____

c) How many football fields (5,351.215104 m²) is this area equivalent to:

_____

d) In 2005 a dam was built to restore the North Aral Sea. Repeat the above steps in order to find the surface areas, in km², of the North Aral Sea for 2004 (before dam construction) and for 2013.

2004 North Aral Sea Surface Area: _____

2013 North Aral Sea Surface Area: _____

source: NASA

e) How could the destruction of the Aral Sea have been prevented in the first place?

_____
_____
_____
_____

Double-click on "Dust Path" under "Question 2."

2- a)Explore the image below. Observe the massive dust-cloud as it heads off the coast of Africa. In what general direction is the dust storm moving? How can you tell?

_____
_____
_____

Double-click on the "Dust Storm video" link.

b) You can see from the video that Saharan dust can travel all the way across the Atlantic to the Caribbean and southeast United States. Using the ruler, measure the distance (in km) from Africa's East coast to the eastern coast of the United States.

source: NASA

Distance:_____

c) Explain why should we care about desertification processes in other parts of the world and in our own country.

_____
_____
_____
_____
_____
_____
_____
_____
_____

In-Lab Activity 3

 In this section, you will create a tour of arid landscapes using the placemarks inside "In-Lab Activity 3" folder. You must use the placemarks made available to you in this folder and describe the landforms, features, or desert types in those placemarks. Here is a quick guide for creating tours.

 ## Step 1 - Create folder

Go to the "Places" panel on the left of the screen and select "my places." Then right-click and select "add" followed by "folder."Name the folder with your last names listed in alphabetic order. Click "ok." All the content that you create for your tour has to be contained here.

 ## Step 2 - Select Points of interest

Explore the placemarks labeled "Location 1" through "Location 6" and select your three favorite ones. Copy the three locations chosen into the folder that you created in the previous step. To copy right-click these places and select "copy." Select your folder, then right-click and then select "paste."

 ## Step 3 Create your own explanation

You can edit the information at each location at any time by right-clicking on the placemark in the places panel and clicking "properties." Change the names and the descriptions of the placemarks that you copied into your folder and create your own. You have to write your own content; you can not simply copy paste text from a website. Use best citation practices. No credit will be given for not following these instructions.

 ## Step 4- Add Photo

Add an image to enhance your placemark. Find a picture of the landform on the web. It does not have to be in the same location as your placemark, but it has to show the same or a related concept. Right-click on the image and copy the URL address of the image ("Copy image address"). Go back to Google Earth Pro, right-click on the placemark in the places panel where you want to attach the image and select "properties." Then select "add web image" and paste the address that you copied, then click "ok." Note: image link address files that end in "jpg," "gif," or "png," will work best. If the photo is not working, make sure you picked one with a link ending in one of these.

 ## Step 5- Email your folder

When you are done, right-click on your folder, choose "Save place as," and save it to the desktop using the guidelines in step 1. Then e-mail this file to your TA.

NOTES

COASTAL LANDFORMS

8

©mivod/shutterstock.com

Skills

Coastal environments are made up of an assortment of landforms exhibited in a spectrum of sizes and shapes ranging from mildly inclined beaches to cliffs. Yet, coastal landforms are best contemplated in two broad categories: erosional and depositional. In fact, the general nature of any coastline may be explained regarding one of these groups. It should be noted, that each of the two major landform types might occur on any given reach of the coast. The purpose of this lab is to teach you to recognize and interpret landform processes that are active in coasts lines. Some of these will be easily identified in sections of the Georgia coast.

Secondary objectives are related to understanding how scientific inquiry works in the context of coastal landform evolution and to be able to make predictions based on your observations.

Extract and measure information

In this lab, you will learn the important skill of extracting and producing data using remote sensing techniques.

Distinguish the coastal landforms

Using many lines of evidence you will be able to identify and describe coastal landforms and the processes that formed them.

Communicate your findings

by sketching and journaling you will be able to share with other students and instructors the most interesting details of your findings.

NOTES

===

🧪 Pre-Lab Activity

Your Name

> 🔍 *This activity will include a selection of places highlighting the different coastal landforms. You will be asked to identify the type of landform you see and some of the factors that lead to their formation. Activate "Pre-Lab Activity" and click "link 1" as a guide.*

🏝️ 1-Click on "Question 1." in the "Pre-Lab Activity" folder. You will find that this landform is a fjord in the country of _____. Approximately how wide is the fjord? What is the difference in elevation from the flat area (A) to the water?

Width (m):_____

Height (m):_____

How are Fjords formed?

_____

_____

_____

_____

🏝️ 2-a) Click on "Question 2." You will find that these landforms are stacks and stumps located in_____. How are they formed? Consult the links in the Pre-Lab Activity for help.

_____

_____

_____

_____

_____

source: Paulo Hidalgo

Stacks and stumps off the Pacific coast of Costa Rica

b) Use the box below to create a flow chart to explain the origin of caves and arches and their relationship to stacks and stumps.

==

3-a) Click on "Question 3". You will find that this Landform is a River Delta located in
_____. How is a river delta formed?(check "link 3" if you need help).

_____

_____

_____

_____

_____

_____

b) Make a drawing of this delta and indicate its dimensions in km.

4-Click on "Question 4". This is a Coral Reef. What role do coral reefs play in island preservation?
What are some of the threats that reefs face? (use "link 4" if you need help)

_____

_____

_____

_____

_____

5-Sea cliffs are abundant in the West coast of North America.
Click "Question 5." What is a sea cliff? Are they an erosional or
depositional feature? How do they form? Use " link 5" if you
need help.

_____

_____

_____

_____

©Kwiatek7/shutterstock.com

6-Summarize depositional and erosional processes that lead to the great variety of coastal landforms that we have today. Provide examples

_____
_____
_____
_____
_____
_____
_____
_____
_____
_____
_____
_____
_____
_____
_____

NOTES

==

 # In-Lab Activity 1

> *Waves, tides, and wind dictate coastal processes and landforms. Streams transport sediment to the coast, where it can be accumulated to form deltas, beaches, dunes, and barrier islands. In this section, you will explore some of these processes.*

1-Click on "Question 1" under "In-Lab Activity 1." This is an Archipelago located in _____. What is an archipelago? (use "link 1" if you need help) What is the approximate length of the archipelago?

_____
_____
_____
_____
_____
_____

2-Click on "Question 2". This is an Isthmus located in_____. Provide a definition (use "link 2" if you need help).

_____
_____
_____
_____
_____
_____

How wide is the Isthmus at the placemark:_____km

What two continents are linked by this Isthmus?_____

3-Click on "Question 3". This is a Barrier Island located in_____. What is a barrier island? Name three reasons they are important to coastal areas and give some examples of barrier islands. Use "link 3" if you need some help.

_____
_____
_____
_____
_____

===

4-Click on "Question 4". This is a Marsh located in _____. Where do marshes typically form? What are they? Explain two of the different kinds of marshes. Use "link 4" if you need help.

_____

_____

_____

_____

_____

_____

_____

_____

5-Click on "Question 5". This is a Gulf. In what country is it located? What is a gulf? Use "link 5" if you need help.
Country:_____

_____

_____

_____

_____

Now, travel to the Gulf of Mexico and explain some of its importance and environmental challenges:

_____

_____

_____

_____

_____

_____

===

 # In-Lab Activity 2

Your Name

> *In this section, we will explore the depositional processes that lead to interesting coastal landforms. However, remember that the combined the action of plate tectonics, wave action, ocean currents and sediment supply controls coastal landforms.*

1-Click on "Question 1." In this location, what is the process responsible for the cuspate shape of this coastal area? In what country is this landscape found? Visit the link if you need some help.

Country:_____

_____

_____

_____

_____

Where is the sediment that is creating this landscape coming from? What is the evidence?

_____

_____

_____

_____

2-Click on "Question 2." In this location, what is the process responsible for the "Hook" shape of this coastal area? In what country or state is this landscape found? Explain your reasoning after watching the animation.

Country:_____

_____

_____

_____

Where is the sediment that is creating this landscape coming from? What is the evidence?

_____

_____

_____

_____

NASA satellite image of Farewell spit.It is located at the northern end of the South Island of New Zealand, running eastwards from Cape Farewell, the island's northernmost point.

source: NASA

===

3-Click on "Question 3." Coral reefs are communities of live organisms that can build spectacular landforms in relatively shallow water depths (<60 m) at low latitudes (<30 degree). Check and Double-click placemark 3.1 and 3.2 to fly to some scenic islands in the South Pacific.What is the name of this Island?

Island Name at placemark 3.1:_____

What kind of reef is surrounding the island? Click on "link 2" if you need help

_____

Click "Placemark 3.2." In what Island is this landscape found? What are the differences when compared to placemark 3.1?

Island Name at placemark 3.2:_____
Differences:_____

_____
_____

4-Click on "Question 4." Barrier islands, beaches, and spits form in areas with abundant sand. Check and Double-click "placemark 1" to fly your next location. Where is it?
Country or State:_____

Place the cursor over placemark 1 to determine the elevation of this point.
Elevation over sea level:_____(m)

How high waves would have to be to top the area specified by the placemark 1.
_____(m)

What is the elevation in the Lagoon side of the barrier island?
_____(m)

Why most of the infrastructure is on the lagoon side of the barrier island?

_____
_____
_____
_____
_____

5-The following photos were acquired by the Operational Land Imager on the Landsat 8 satellite in the shoal area off Cape Point. The sequence shows the sands drifting and accumulated into a new location in November 2016. In January 2017, the image shows the formation of waves that are breaking on the shallow water off the tip of the cape. The place of those breakers is where the island eventually formed. The third image, taken this month, shows the island formed, and nearly a mile in length.

Using your pen, indicate with arrows the ocean current direction in the 3 images. Also, indicate areas of low current velocity in the 3 images.

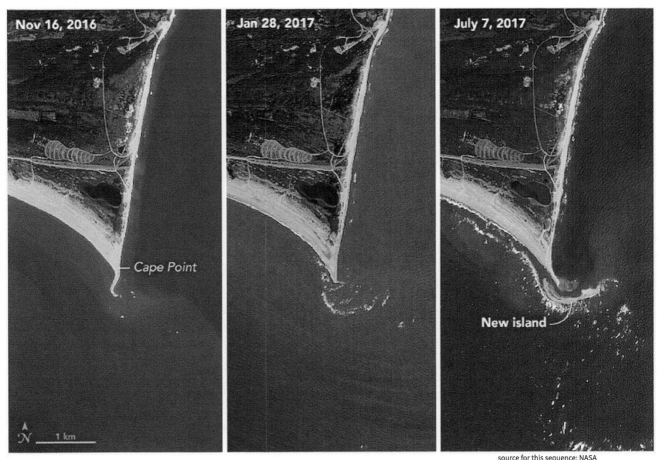

source for this sequence: NASA

Figuratively, Dare County where this new Island is located, is thinking of building a lighthouse and a park. What would you recommend the city officials after looking at the historical record preserved in remote sensing images in Google Earth Pro? Click the icon for historical imagery to see the coastal evolution of this location.

_____

_____

_____

_____

_____

_____

_____

==

6-Click on "Question 6." Here this island is being reshaped by longshore currents. What is the name of the island?

Island Name:_____

What is the direction of the longshore currents? How can you tell? (in which direction is the island growing). Consult historical imagery if you have doubts.

_____
_____
_____
_____

Make a diagram of the Island and indicate on it places of deposition and places where erosion takes place along the shoreline. Also indicate with arrow the direction of the currents.

7-Click on "Question 7."Jetties can be installed to prevent sand erosion. Where is the location where these jetties have been installed?.

Country/Province/State:_____

In which direction is the current moving the sand? How can you tell?

_____
_____
_____
_____

Make a diagram of the, shore, the jetties and the currents.

==

 # In-Lab Activity 3

 You are well on your way to becoming a costal processes expert! You will now be asked to apply what you have learned about costal geomorphology.

1-Zoom to the coast of Georgia and click "Point 1" in the "In-Lab Activity 3" folder. Zoom in. To the northeast of this Island, there is another Island. What are the names of these islands?
Name of the Islands:_____

What is the grayish-brown area that separates these two islands?
_____
_____

Notice the lines of trees on one of the Islands, why are they in that formation? Look at the features in the northeast corner of the northern island if you need a hint)
_____
_____
_____
_____

2-Now, Click "point 2" and go to the opening of the tidal estuary. Notice that there is a clock icon in the toolbox. Click on it. Move the slider back to 1988. Your map has transported you back in time to the year 1988. Use the scroll bar to travel through the years so that you can see the changes to the estuary.

What how far is the opening of the 1988 estuary from the opening of the 2016 estuary?
_____m

From 1988 to 2016, in which direction is the opening moving and why?
_____
_____
_____

During which year(s) do you see more changes happening to the opening of the estuary? What were those changes?
_____
_____
_____
_____
_____

==

3-Go back to 1988 on your time scrollbar and then zoom to point 3 and you will notice that the estuary is on the backside of the beach. Measure the distance from the ocean shoreline to the east bank of the estuary (use your Google Earth ruler). What is the distance?
_____m

Now, fast-forward in time to 2012 and take that measurement again. Has this area been eroding or growing?Explain

_____

_____

How much has eroded or has been added?
_____m

At this rate, in what year will that estuary cut through to the ocean?
_____

What will likely happen to the current opening?Explain

_____

_____

_____

_____

4-Now, Click "point 4" and calculate the area of this island using the ruler tool. What is the area?
_____m²

Click on the clock icon in the toolbox. Click on it. Move the slider back to 1988. Your map has transported you back in time to the year 1988. Use the scroll bar to move through the years so that you can see the changes to the island. What were the areas of the Island in the following years:

1988:_____m² 1993:_____m² 1999:_____m² 2017:_____m²

Taking in to account the sizes of the island in 1988 and in 2017, what is the growth rate?
_____m²/year

In this activity we have determine that barrier islands are prone to dynamic and fast changes. Explain what controls the growth and erosion of barrier islands.

_____

_____

_____

_____

_____

NOTES

©SoRad/shutterstock.com

9 OCEANS AND TIDES

Objectives

Tides and oceans can reshape the coastline. This process can act in timescales of millions of years or in some cases this process can happen quickly. The role of tides as a landscape modifier is essential whenever sediment transport is involved as significant amounts of sediment may erode and remodel the coastline. Also, the rise and fall of tides allocate wave energy across a shore zone altering the depth of water and the location of the shoreline. In this lab, you will observe the typical landforms found in the ocean and their relationship with tides and currents. Finally, we will explore some of the environmental challenges that are threatening the hydrosphere and the Earth system.

Concepts

| Bathymetric Features | Tides and Currents | Natural Hazards | Environmental Challenges |

==

Core Concepts

©Marc Ward/shutterstock.com

©Fotos593/shutterstock.com

©Haverpino/shutterstock.com

Bathymetric features
Association with tectonics

Tides and Currents
Wind and moon cycles

Environment
What have we done?

Mid-Ocean Ridges

————————————➤

Trenches

————————————➤

Continental Slope

————————————➤

Continental Shelf

————————————➤

Abyssal Plain

————————————➤

Spring Tide

————————————➤

Neap Tide

————————————➤

Thermohaline Circulation

————————————➤

Ocean Currents

————————————➤

Acidification

————————————➤

Rising Temperatures

————————————➤

Pollution

————————————➤

Eutrophication

————————————➤

Learning outcomes

After completing this lab, you will know the variety of the ocean floor's landform features, and how tides and currents act together to distribute through thermohaline circulation nutrients that are indispensable for marine life. Also, you will learn about the most challenging environmental problems that the oceans face and why we should, as a planet, get together and try to find solutions to these issues.

NOTES

Pre-Lab Activity

Your Name

When you open your Google Earth Pro application, one of the striking features of these satellite photos is that the Earth glows blue. A little more than 70% of the Earth's surface is covered by water. The oceans on Earth are vast, yet we know more about outer space than we do about our oceans. The importance of oceans is paramount, without oceans, there would be no life, as oceans regulate Earth's climate and recycle chemical elements in the Earth system. Let's explore the oceans!

This activity will include a selection of places highlighting the different seafloor landforms. You will be asked to identify the type of landform you see and some of the factors that lead to their formation. Use "link 1" as a guide. Activate "Pre-Lab Activity." Play video if you need help.

1-Click on "Question 1." Remember back to your previous labs on plate tectonics. Match points 1 to 7 to the given names below and give a brief explanation on how they are formed. formed?

Mid-Ocean Ridge:

_____

Continental Shelf:

_____

Continental Slope:

_____

Active Continental Margin:

_____

Passive Continental Margin:

_____

Oceanic trench:

_____

Abyssal Plain:

_____

==

2-Open the "Question 2" folder and look at the "cross-section line." Sketch a cross section of the ocean floor elevation along that line. Label the different areas of your cross-section using the applicable terms from question 1. What type of margins (active/Passive) lies along this transect?

Type of Continental Margin:_____

3-Click on "Question 3."What type of mass wasting is going on at point 3? Use the measurement tool to measure the area (in km^2) of this landform. (Hint: Click on the link to learn more about this landform.)

Mass wasting type: _____

Area in km^2:_____

What natural hazard is usually associated with events like this one?.

_____
_____
_____

4-Open "Question 4" folder and look at the "cross-section line." Sketch a cross-section of the ocean floor elevation along that line. Describe the types of landforms this line transects as part of your answer.

Type of Continental Margin:_____

==

 In-Lab Activity 1 ————————————

Your Name

 Tides are important modifiers of the coastline. Here you will understand how they operate and what controls them. In this section, you will explore how tides interact with the coastal landforms and why should we care about this interaction.

1-Open "In-Lab Activity 1" folder and double click on "point 1" under "question 1" and watch the short video on tides. What is the primary factor that influences tidal action? What are spring tides and neap tides?

_____

_____

_____

_____

Draw a diagram that describes how tides work. Be sure to include the sun and the moon in the diagram.

2-Navigate to point 2 inside folder "Question 2". This area is the Bay of Fundy, which has the largest tides on Earth. Why does this area experience higher tides than an area in open water like Hawaii? (Hint: Watch the video attached to this placemark to get additional information.)

_____

_____

_____

This image provides a view of the striking difference between low and high tides in the Bay of Fundy, Nova Scotia. During low tide, boats are entirely exposed.

©V J Matthew/shutterstock.com

===

Activate 'Question 3" and activate the "Tide Prediction" checkbox.

3-Navigate to "Point 1" inside folder "Question 3". Observe which tidal station is the closest to Point 1.

What is the name of this station:_____

Click on the station and then click on "Daily" tide prediction.

How many high tides and low tides are there in one day?

_____

What is the time interval that separates a low tide from a high tide?

_____

In the station that you clicked, at what time do the high tides occur? Do they occur always at the same time everyday? Explain. Click again on the station and instead of "daily" click "weekly." This will help you answer the question.

_____

_____

_____

_____

_____

_____

_____

_____

According to the current tide height in the station at this precise time of the day, report if the locations in folder "Question 3" are experiencing high tide or low tide.

Station Name:_____(Same as above)

Current Time:_____Current Tide:_____

Enter the name of the countries and indicate a "H" for high tide and a "L" for low tide. :

Location 1:_____Location 2:_____

Location 3:_____Location 4:_____

In-Lab Activity 2

In this section, we will explore the hazard of tsunamis. These events can cause great loss of property and life. The damage that they bring to coastal areas is severe. These events can cause damage thousands of kilometers away from the event that originated the tsunami.

1-Before we understand what happens during tsunami events, it is necessary to take a look into how waves change their amplitude as they move through the ocean. Explore the wave amplitude links and animations inside "Question 1" contained in the folder "In-Lab Activity 2".

Why do waves get taller as they approach the coast?

_____

_____

_____

Now click on the link in the "Question 1 folder" to learn about tsunamis. Watch the video and define it here. Include the causes of tsunamis in your answer.Use the figure below to help you define a tsunami.

_____

_____

_____

_____

_____

_____

_____

_____

_____

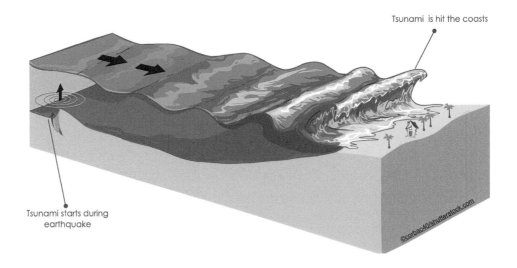

Tsunami is hit the coasts

Tsunami starts during earthquake

©corbac40/shutterstock.com

===

2-Tsunamis may affect areas far away from the event that started them. Open the "Question 2" folder and list five countries located more than 500 km away from the source of this 2004 tsunami in Indonesia that could potentially have received higher than average waves possibly creating damage and loss of life.

_____

_____

_____

Now click on the link "Tsunami Hazards" in the "Question 2 folder." Why is there a higher risk of experiencing a tsunami in the Pacific Ocean compared to the Atlantic?

_____

_____

_____

_____

In the Pacific, what country is more susceptible to tsunamis? Describe one of these events including the date that it happened, the magnitude of the earthquake that triggered the event, fatalities, injuries, and loss of property.

_____

_____

_____

_____

3-Activate the "Tsunami travel times" overlay inside "Question 3" folder and double-click on it. Where was the tsunami-triggering event located (country/State)?

_____

If you were at locations 1,2 and 3; how long do you have to prepare for the arrival of the tsunami?

Location 1 country: _____Distance to source:_____km
Hours before arrival: _____
Location 2 country: _____Distance to source:_____km
Hours before arrival: _____
Location 3 country: _____Distance to source:_____km
Hours before arrival: _____

Why do locations 2 and 3 have similar arriving times even though they are located at very different distances from the event that originated the tsunami?

_____

_____

_____

In-Lab Activity 3

Humans and oceans have been in a long-standing relationship. Humans modify ocean's conditions, and the biological and thermal conditions of the ocean affect humans. Around 40 percent of the United States population lives near an ocean. These areas contribute with approximately $6.6 trillion dollars a year to the countries economy. The importance of oceans in the earth system is paramount, and human affectations by oceans are inevitable. Population growth, climate change, acidification of the oceans, and eutrophication are some of the challenges that our coastal communities face.

1-In this question, we will explore ocean temperature anomalies. An anomaly is when something is distinct from typical, or standard . A sea surface temperature anomaly (SST) is how different the ocean temperature at a precise area at a specific time is from the normal temperatures for that region. Open the folder "Question 1" inside "In-Lab Activity 3." Expand "Sea surface Temperature" and switch to "SST" anomaly. This animation created by NASA can tell you if the oceans are warming or cooling. Based on the global patterns that you observe, would you say that Earth's oceans are for the most part abnormally hot or cold? Explain how your conclusion makes sense agreeing with other observations that have been made in other Earth systems around the world.

_____
_____
_____
_____

Why is a warming ocean a "bad thing"? Click on the link if you need some ideas.

_____
_____
_____
_____

How can a warming ocean lead to more powerful and larger storms?

_____
_____
_____
_____

Overview of three hurricanes Irma, Jose and Katia in the Caribbean Sea and the Atlantic Ocean

©lavizzara/shutterstock.com

===

2-In this question, we will explore thermohaline circulation, a great conveyor belt that moves enormous amounts of water (more than all the rivers in the world combined) and circulates nutrients and energy around the world. What is thermohaline circulation and how does it work? Visit the link inside Question 2 for more information.

_____

_____

_____

_____

_____

_____

In the previous question, you determined that the temperatures in the oceans are rising, this matches also was has been quantified on land. Could the rising ocean temperature disturb the thermohaline circulation? Explain. Visit the link inside "question 2" for some help.

_____

_____

_____

3-Another effect that impact of human activities has on the health of oceans is the rise in number and increase in area of marine dead zones. What are they? Visit the link inside "Question 3" for more information.

_____

_____

_____

_____

Why do dead zones occur? Explain Eutrophication and some of its causes.

_____

_____

_____

_____

Why should we care about this phenomenon? Is it reversible? How?

_____

_____

_____

_____

==

4-In this question, we will explore sea level trends. Activate "Question 4" and make sure the "Sea level trends" is activated. Determine if the sea levels recorded by NOAA gauging stations indicate: Neutral conditions, raising sea levels, or sea level drop.

North America: _____

What is the most common amount of expected sea level change?_____

Where is it expected to raise the most? and by how much_____

_____

What is the value of the confidence interval (click on the arrow)?_____

Asia: _____

What is the most common amount of expected sea level change?_____

Where is it expected to raise the most? and by how much_____

_____

What is the value of the confidence interval (click on the arrow)?_____

Click on link "sea level rise explained." Tide gauge readings, core sample of coastal deposits, and satellite imagery indicate that over the past century the Global Mean Sea Level has been rising. What is the average of this rise in centimeters?

_____(cm)

What is provoking this sea level rise? and by what 3 mechanisms is the sea level rising?

_____

_____

_____

_____

List a few consequences and hazards associated with sea level rise?

_____

_____

_____

_____

Coastal erosion at Skipsea, Yorkshire.

©Matthew J Thomas/shutterstock.com

NOTES

NOTES

GLACIAL LANDFORMS

©Arcady/shutterstock.com

10

Skills

You will use Google Earth Pro and online resources to explore glacial landforms around the world and the erosive or depositional mechanisms that developed them. Also, you will examine the effects of climate change in polar regions, including the periodic and longer-term fluctuations in the extent of the ice cap in the North Pole. Finally, you will be able to predict how the collapse of ice shelves may affect shipping pathways, access to fossil fuels, biological organisms, and local climate variations due to changes in ocean currents.

Core concepts

source: Paulo Hidalgo

Erosional Landforms

Cirques, U-Shaped Valleys, Aretes, etc. These are produced by the direct action of ice or liquid water derived from glacial melting.

source: Paulo Hidalgo

Depositional Landforms

Eskers, Kames, Moraines, Outwash fans, Drumlins, etc. These are formed when ice or whatever have lost some of the potency and can no longer carry sediments.

source: Paulo Hidalgo

Global Warming

Climate change is a ubiquitous subject in the media, and its outcome is anticipated to present significant challenges for human society. Hence, you need to develop an awareness of the issues linked to this phenomenon.

NOTES

===

_____
Your Name

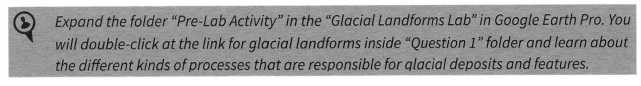

Erosion by glaciers is a constant reminder that no rock can withstand the geologic agents that shape them, especially when the action of these agents is protracted. The resulting fragments, such as rock and ice, move under the forces of gravity and deposit in areas where the conditions are more favorable for depositional glacial landforms.

 # Pre-Lab Activity

Expand the folder "Pre-Lab Activity" in the "Glacial Landforms Lab" in Google Earth Pro. You will double-click at the link for glacial landforms inside "Question 1" folder and learn about the different kinds of processes that are responsible for glacial deposits and features.

 1- a) List and explain what type of processes lead to the formation of erosive glacial landforms.

_____
_____
_____
_____
_____

b) Describe 3 landforms that are formed by deposition of glacial derived sediments

_____
_____
_____
_____
_____

c) After consulting the link indicated above, identify the features in the following images:

Weird white water	Large Block	Groovy!

source: Paulo Hidalgo	source: Paulo Hidalgo	©Bob Hare/shutterstock.com

_____   _____   _____

Double-click and expand "Question 2." Use the locations within the folder to complete the following question.

 2-Define the following landforms and then click and match "Location 1, Location 2, Location 3, etc." in the Question 2 folder with the name of its corresponding landform.

Cirque

Location:_____

Definition:_____

_____

_____

U-Shaped valley

Location:_____

Definition:_____

_____

_____

Arete

Location:_____

Definition:_____

_____

_____

Kettle lake

Location:_____

Definition:_____

_____

_____

Outwash fan

Location:_____

Definition:_____

_____

_____

Moraine

Location:_____

Definition:_____

_____

_____

Horn

Location:_____

Definition:_____

_____

_____

In-Lab Activity 1

 *In this section, you will create a tour of a glaciated region of your choice using the places around the placemarks inside "In-Lab Activity 1" folder. You **must** use one of these glacier systems and describe the location, landforms, features, glacial processes, etc.. Here is a quick guide for creating tours.*

Step 1 - Create folder

Go to the "Places" panel on the left of the screen and select "my places." Then right-click and select "add" followed by "folder." Name the folder with your last names listed in alphabetic order. Click "ok." All the content that you create for your tour has to be contained here.

Step 2 - Select Points of interest

Explore the placemarks inside "In-Lab Activity 1" and select your favorite glacier. Explore the area around your chosen glacier and try to spot glacial landforms. You must find three erosional and three depositional glacial landforms. Create place marks for all of them. When you have found suitable locations for your tour, play around with the zoom and the tilt to get the best view possible for your landforms.

Step 3 Create your own explanation

You can edit the information at each location at any time by right-clicking on the placemark in the places panel and clicking "properties." Give names and descriptions to the placemarks that you created. You have to write your own content; you can not simply copy paste text from a website. Use best citation practices. No credit will be given for not following these instructions.

Step 4- Add Photo

Add an image to enhance your placemark. Find a picture of the landform. In the "layers" panel in Google Earth Pro, activate photos to find pictures of the feature that you are highlighting. It does not have to be in the same location as your placemark, but it has to show the same or a related concept. Right-click on the image and copy the URL address of the image ("Copy image address"). Go back to Google Earth Pro, right-click on the placemark in the places panel where you want to attach the image and select "properties." Then select "add web image" and paste the address that you copied, then click "ok." Note: image link address files that end in "jpg," "gif," or "png," will work best. If the photo is not working, make sure you picked one with a link ending in

Step 5- Email your folder

When you are done, right-click on your folder, choose "Save place as," and save it to the desktop using the guidelines in step 1. Then e-mail this file to your TA.

🧪 In-Lab Activity 2

💡 *The National Snow and Ice Data Center (NSIDC) performs and supports research and makes scientific information available concerning the parts of the Earth that are typically frozen, which collectively make up the cryosphere. In this activity, we will study changes that are occurring in the cryosphere by examining maps and other information from NSIDC and other sources.*

🔖 *In this section, you will use information from numerous web sites to examine the consequences of climate change in polar regions. You will learn to use satellite and aerial imagery, maps, graphs, and statistics to understand tendencies associated to changes in the Earth system.*

⛰️ 1- Perform a search on the web for a definition of the Northwest Passage. Summarize that definition in a few lines.

_____

_____

_____

_____

_____

⛰️ 2- In Google Earth ,click on "Question 2" under "In-Lab Activity 2." . This link will take you to a page that discusses various environmental changes that are occurring in the Arctic. What are some of them, and how may they affect other parts of the world?

_____

_____

_____

_____

_____

_____

_____

⛰️ 3- In Google Earth, click on "Question 3". From this website, answer what growth or shrinking trends in sea ice extent are currently being observed?

_____

_____

_____

_____

_____

_____

_____

===

4- In Google Earth click on "Question 4." From this resource answer how is climate change changing the maritime transportation in the Arctic?

_____
_____
_____
_____
_____

5-In Google Earth, select the Google Earth ruler tool and then select "path."

a- Measure in kilometers the shortest route by ship, between Japan and Germany. Avoid going through the Arctic Ocean.

_____

b- Measure in kilometers the shortest route by ship, between Alaska and New York. Avoid going through the Arctic Ocean.

_____

6-Inspect the daily image update in the "Arctic Sea Ice News and Analysis" page of the NSIDC (click on Question 6). Note: if the link won't load, right click this link in the "places" panel, click "properties," and copy and paste the link address into a separate internet browser.

a- During what time of the year is the Arctic sea ice extent normally at its lowest? Explain the connection to seasonal cycles.

_____
_____
_____
_____
_____
_____

b- Inspecting data from 1979 to 2000, What was the average extent of sea ocean with at least 15% of sea ice (in millions of square kilometers)

_____
_____
_____
_____

===

c- What was the average area of ocean with at least 15% of sea ice (same units as before), at the start of this past May?

_____

7-In Google Earth, activate and expand the NSIDC virtual globes. Activate "September 1979 to 2013." This will display the change of ice coverage from September 1979 to 2013. Progressively move the time slider at the top of the 3D Viewer. Do it slowly. What is the overall variation in sea ice coverage for September 1979 to 2013?

_____

_____

_____

_____

_____

8-Click on placemark 3.8a and 3.8b.

a- What significant event in the Arctic was exposed by satellite images?

_____

b- After this event, how long is the shortest distance by ship, in kilometers, between Japan and Germany?

_____

c- After this event, how long is the shortest distance by ship, in kilometers, between northern New York and Northern Alaska?

_____

9-Activate "Greenland ice melt, 1980 to 2007."

a- Expand the folder and then click on time animation. Move the slider and pay attention to the colors and compare to the color scale on the side. Describe the tendency in maximum annual melt extent.

_____

_____

==

b-What has been the trend, over time, concerning the area in Greenland that has suffered 60 or more melt days during a calendar year?

_____

10-Click on placemark 3.10. Answer the following questions:
a- Explain how thawing of Arctic ice may lead to climate change in North America and Europe? (Read the document, do not try the audio.)

_____
_____
_____
_____
_____

11-Click placemarks 3.11a, 3.11b, and 3.11c. Answer the following questions:

a- What consequence is the ice decline having on the ecosystem and the lives of polar bears?

_____
_____
_____
_____

b- Using the Polar Bear Habitat map, what is the long-term tendency in frequency of occurrence of polar bear habitat?

_____
_____
_____
_____

c-Explain why the State of Alaska decided to contest the entry of polar bears as a threatened species by the federal government?

_____
_____
_____
_____

12- List positive and negative effects connected to variations in polar ice conditions that were presented in this exercise. In your view, what actions could authorities, companies, organizations, and individuals take to mitigate or benefit from these conditions?

_____

_____

_____

_____

_____

_____

_____

_____

_____

_____

_____

_____

_____

_____

_____